FOR

Everett

Marina

Max

Jordan

Shea

Izzy

Ella Rose (ER)

Eden

Liliana

Troy

Leo

Griffin

TABLE OF CONTENTS

ABOUT
THE STARDUST MYSTERY PROJECT

This illustrated science adventure book is one product of a National Science Foundation (NSF) project (Award #1738291) whose objective was to provide a good way for children to learn science through transmedia storytelling. The book is for readers age eight to fourteen. It is a fictional time-travel adventure of young characters that are discovering non-fiction science concepts. Their adventures in a *Virtual World* are their favorite activities as they cope with the hardships of the Covid-19 pandemic. The *Race to the Big Bang* is the sequel to *The Stardust Mystery* illustrated science story book published in 2020. The *Stardust Mystery Project* combines books, time-travel adventure video games, and science videos featuring the book characters. The central science theme of the project is STARDUST (atoms), its creation during the evolution of the universe, and its sharing during the history of planet Earth. The *Race to the Big Bang* expands the science concepts as the book's young characters discover unusual things on earth, in the solar system, and in the universe. They help prove the *Big Bang* theory by measuring the shrinking distance to a nearby galaxy as they travel back in time. They experience Einstein's Twin Paradox. They turn a planet that they have found 7 billion years ago into their space station by applying some of the strategies that made Planet Earth habitable. Their planet accidentally provides a wonderful example of the *Survival of the Fittest* principal of the *Theory of Evolution*. The Cosmic Kids end their adventure with a new project. They use the *Virtual World* to create videos to help other kids understand how we can become infected by the Covid-19 virus, and how a vaccine can keep us safe. They learn some interesting biology in the process. Information on the *Stardust Mystery Project* and links to the video games and videos can be found on TheBeamer LLC's web site: https://TheStardust-Mystery.com. Science videos and game trailers are available on the STARDUST MYSTERY YouTube channel. Links to these resources are on our web site and at the end of the book.

ACKNOWLEDGMENTS

First the author would like to thank the four cousins—Shea, Izabella, Ella Rose, and Eden—Peter and Sally Solomon's grandchildren, whose personalities and accomplishments have been the inspiration for the four cousin characters in the book. Joselyn Linder did a wonderful job of adding depth to the characters as she edited the manuscript. Thank you to Tom Lucatorto, Stephen Shamroth, Elizabeth Shamroth, Judy Goodman, Alana Brady, and William Wang for providing feedback on the story in general and for the physics, chemistry, biology, education, and medical information, in particular. My family was always there with guidance and advice. Thank you, Joanne Solomon, Jeffrey Solomon, Sally Solomon, Sara Ringler, Michele Caton, and grandkids Liliana, Troy, Leo, and Griffin. Many of the book's illustrations and chapter stories were derived from two video games: MissionKT and Building the Universe that feature the book characters as avatars. A huge thank-you goes to Professor Robert McCloud and his team at Sacred Heart University, to Andrew Nelson and his team at Half Full Nelson, LLC, and to Professor Kenneth Thompson and his team at the University of Connecticut for the production of the MissionKT video game. Another huge thank-you goes to Professor Keo Heng and his team at Becker College for production of the Building the Universe video game and for production of the science, trailer, and How-To animated videos starring the book characters. Finally, thank you Lori Conser from Wheatmark Publishing for your help in the final production of the book.

PART 1
PANDEMIC LOCKDOWN
(APRIL)

FEELING LOW DOWN

(AS TOLD BY LIZZY)

Four months ago, at the end of December, I had the best, most exciting week of my life. I got to go on a way cool trip to the moon with my family and friends. The moon trip was a prize for my team, the *Cosmic Kids*, coming in second in the *Science and the Future Contest* sponsored by a company called Time and Space, Inc. (TSI for short). Lately, I have been doing a lot of thinking about our wonderful trip, and how I got to go.

First of all, the contest was for teams of up to four. The worst part was that it had to be made up of *family members* who were thirteen years old or younger. My obnoxious cousin Milo was thirteen, like me, my sweet cousin VC was twelve, and my annoying sister Neddy was eleven. Luckily, we had the best coach, our scientist grandpa. Miraculously, we ended up having a great time, and we learned a lot of cool science.

In the *Regionals*, we competed against other teams in the northeast. We had to come up with the best invention for the future. Our invention came in first for all the regions. We couldn't believe it, even though it was way, *way* cool.

It was called the *Beamer Virtual World*, named after Grandpa's favorite TV show *Star Trek*, which has a famous line, "Beam me up Scotty." Our idea was a super-cool website where you could sign in and choose an avatar that visits any space and time ever. Imagine, you could feel like you are anywhere in the universe,

at any time, and your friends could even join you there! I loved that you could also make yourself any size you wanted to. You could crush the Leaning Tower of Pisa with your enormous feet or become so small that you disappear like a mouse into the toga of an ancient Greek scholar. You could even speak to people who lived there.

During the contest, we showed VC and me visiting a brilliant astronomer named Galileo. It was in Italy in the year 1590. We submitted a picture of the two of us talking to Galileo in front of the Leaning Tower of Pisa. We kept our avatars the normal size and didn't crush anything. What we wanted to show was that we could ask him questions. The coolest part was that Galileo's avatar would be able to respond using information on the internet that the actual Galileo knew! Our idea was that any kid would be able to learn things from the very people who had studied them and shared them with the world. *People like Galileo!*

TSI loved our invention so much that they programmed the *Beamer Virtual World* for everyone to use in the *Finals*, which was about <u>*The Stardust Mystery*</u>. We learned something incredible: *we are made of stardust that was once in the bodies of Albert Einstein and the Last T-Rex.*

First, we had to figure out what stardust was, where, when, and how it was created, and how it got from Einstein and the Last T-Rex into us. Our avatars in the *Virtual World* had roles like *Scientist* or *Navigator* with tools and scientific instruments like composition, velocity, and temperature analysis to help figure it all out. Even though they drive me nuts, I actually loved working with my cousins to solve the mystery. I loved playing in the virtual worlds, and I loved competing. I also loved getting to know the other teams and having fun with them.

We came in second because another team found out the answers more quickly than we did. Luckily, they have become two of my best friends. Jackson Graham and his sister Johari from the Pacific Region beat us. We met them when we traveled to California for the Regionals presentations. We couldn't feel too bad about losing to them because Jackson was this boy genius who was already in college at age thirteen. He was studying physics at Caltech, so he already knew a lot about stardust. TSI also let us go on the moon trip with them because we agreed to sell them our *Beamer Virtual World* invention. The team that came in third was the *Brooklyn Bunch*. They were siblings, two sets of twins who came from Brooklyn but who were all born in Russia. The older twins were identical, and the younger ones were brother and sister twins, which are called *fraternal twins*. Milo had an enormous and disgusting crush on Svetlana, one of the older twins.

I have two pictures from the moon trip on my wall. One is of the rocket ship passengers just before we took off. That's me on the right. Next to me are Jackson and Johari. Then comes Grandpa, who was our team coach; my cousin Milo; my grandma; and the rest of my team: my cousin VC and my sister, Neddy. The other picture is from when we reached the moon and looked back on our beautiful Planet Earth. It was so cool.

It was the most amazing trip ever. It took us five whole days: two to get there, one to spin around and two to get back. Everyone was excited. Being weightless was so way cool. Every time I looked out the window at the moon up close or our planet so far away, it took my breath away. The whole way there, we played games and talked and joked. Neddy, the space nerd, offered all kinds of facts about what we were seeing. We teased Milo about his crush on Svetlana

and listened to Johari complain about living with the "boy genius." I asked how he could be such a genius if I always kept beating him at gin rummy. So, Johari started teasing Jackson about that. We four cousins talked about all the great vacations we had taken with Grandpa and Grandma. The whole moon trip was just the coolest, period.

After we came home, things started returning to normal. We went back to school, but we were all still so excited about the trip. We walked around with smiles on our faces, and all our classmates wanted to hear about our adventure. Milo and I were now in high school, but our middle-school principal, Dr. Evil, invited us back to join VC and Neddy at a school assembly to talk about the trip. That made us decide she's probably not so evil after all.

We showed pictures and talked about all the exciting things we saw and did. Milo talked about his awesome ride on top of a rocket roaring off from Earth and leaving our atmosphere. Neddy, of course, described in detail the experience of being weightless. I described the amazing scenes out the window as we circled the moon, and VC had everyone at the edge of their seats as she talked about the fiery and scary reentry into Earth's atmosphere.

It was such an amazing time. I honestly wish it could have lasted forever because pretty much right after we got back, that's when everything began to fall apart. That's when it seemed like there would never be another adventure, ever again. That's when Covid-19 hit, and all of us had to stay in our houses and be basically alone. Or, even worse, people we loved became very, terrifyingly sick.

We definitely weren't on the moon anymore. And, honestly, everything became the least cool it possibly could.

▰▰▰▰▰

I felt worse than I had ever felt in my whole life. I started having bad dreams, and I didn't want to get up in the morning. My room seemed to be getting smaller and smaller.

I thought I had depression.

It was March when the bad stuff started to happen. First it was hearing the news about the Covid-19 Coronavirus pandemic. Then, the second week in March, my dad got really sick. He went to the hospital emergency room and got tested. Yep, he had the virus. The pandemic had come to Connecticut. Mom quarantined him in the basement. I had to wear a mask over my nose and mouth when I went down to visit him. He looked terrible, and it made me feel so bad.

Then Grandpa got sick and went to the hospital, where we were not allowed to visit. I was so worried about both of them, and I cried when I thought about what was happening to them. I cried when I looked at Mom's worried face too. My sister seemed to be handling all this much better than me and kept trying to cheer me up.

"Hey sis," said Neddy as she came into our room and gave me a hard stare through her huge glasses perched at the end of her nose. "You have to stop moping around. Let's ride our bikes down to the hospital. Mom said that Grandpa is feeling much better."

"What for?" I asked. "It isn't like we can even visit him."

"I know," she replied, "but we can stand outside and wave at him. That might cheer us all up."

I thought about her idea and sat up. "OK," I said as I dragged myself out of bed. "I'm in."

I got dressed and we got our bikes out. It was a sunny day, but it was early spring, so it was still very cold. The ride immediately lifted my mood. When we got to the hospital, there was a big sign on the door saying we had to wear a mask and use hand sanitizer. A table next to the door had both. Neddy and I each put on a mask and rubbed our hands together with the hand sanitizer. Then we went inside. A lady at a desk saw us and told us we weren't allowed in the hospital because of the pandemic. We told her about Grandpa, and Neddy even managed to muster up a few tears. I'd been crying for fourteen days straight so it was no problem for me.

The lady told us to go back outside and showed us where to stand. Then she called Grandpa's nurse. It took what felt like a long time, but finally Grandpa appeared at a window on the second floor. We shouted. "Hello," but he couldn't hear us. So we waved and gestured back and forth for about twenty minutes. Neddy communicated that I was sad by making a sad face and pointing at me. Grandpa shook his fist and shook his head no. He made a big, exaggerated smile, and that made me laugh and smile too. I felt better. We both bowed theatrically to say goodbye and Grandpa laughed. Then he coughed which made me worry. But then he smiled again and gave us a thumbs up. We headed home.

"Thanks, Neddy," I said as we rode home. "That was a great idea."

But there was more bad news on April Fool's Day that was no April fool's joke. Our schools both closed for real. Neddy and I were confined to the house with no friends, and no other family besides our mom and dad. Dad was still in quarantine but feeling much better. Now everyone had to wear masks if we went out or anyone came into the house. The bad dreams started again, and the days got long and boring. I was getting more and more depressed, and I had no Idea what to do about it. The only thing that seemed to help was staring at the two pictures on my wall and daydreaming about the contest and the moon trip. That made me a tiny bit happier.

Then, two days after the hospital visit, my sister came to the rescue again. She was the first one to see something that was going to help us all get through this difficult time. I was so excited. For the first time in ages, I got out of bed without anyone having to tell me to.

THE RACE TO THE BIG BANG

(AS TOLD BY NEDDY)

"Lizzy, Lizzy, Lizzy," I screamed as I ran into our room. "We are saved!"

Lizzy, as usual for the last few weeks, was not out of bed yet, even though it was eleven o'clock in the morning. She was just staring at the two pictures on the wall over her bed. Her long red hair was in a wild scatter around her head, not in her usual single braid.

I know my sister can be really moody. She was in a bad mood for half of last year because she felt responsible for getting Grandpa fired from his job as a science teacher at our middle school. It was because of the famous watermelon catastrophe.

I tried again a little louder when she ignored me. "Look what we just got in the mail from TSI. They are running a new contest!"

She turned and faced the ceiling with a blank stare. I put the thick envelope on top of her nose. "I think she moved," I murmured. "Yes, she is conscious. Lizzy, can you hear me? Lizzy are you in there somewhere?"

"OK, sis," she snapped, giving me her meanest stare. "Very funny. You're a real riot."

But she took the envelope off of her nose and opened it. As she read the announcement, her expression changed from scowling, to bland, excited, and then happy. "Wow," she squealed, "way cool! I love it. I guess I owe you a thank-you again."

"This contest can be a great cure for the pandemic blahs," I said, jumping on her bed. "It won't be a waste of time because we will be learning lots of science. And look at the grand prize!"

The grand prize was one million dollars in cash and up to one million dollars in college scholarships to share among the team members. And there was even cash and a million dollars in scholarships for both the second and third place teams. There was also a twenty-five thousand dollar cash prize for winning the *Regionals*. In the first contest, there was no cash prize. Then again, we did get to take a trip to the moon, which is something only twelve people before us had ever done!

"This could be better than the original *Science and the Future Contest* about stardust," Lizzy added, miraculously sitting up. "We get to use the *Beamer* again!" She started rambling about stuff I already knew, like how we'd have to build a virtual space station for our team to use when we went back seven billion years in time. She squealed about how the best space station would win the *Regionals* competition. And if we won, we'd get to travel back to the *Big Bang* to build the first atoms in the universe! "The team that completes all the missions in the least time wins the *Finals*," Lizzy said finally, ending her ramble. I didn't mind her talking, to be honest. It was great to hear her sounding excited.

"The rules are different from the first contest," I added. "Team members can be up to age eighteen, and they don't have to be in the same family. And we can have any number of coaches."

"Cool," said Lizzy. "So who should be on our team?"

"Well, let's start with the *Cosmic Kids* team," I suggested. "That's a must. And Grandpa, of course, will be a coach."

"Let's ask Jackson and Johari to join us," Lizzy added. "They would add lots of brain power."

"And I would like to ask Richie to join us too," I said. I know it's weird that Richie and I have become good friends. You might remember that last year he was the biggest bully ever, especially to me. But Dr. Evil made him apologize for bullying me in school, and after that we became good friends. I guess Richie always felt jealous that everyone thought I was so smart. He felt pretty insecure, even though he's one of the best artists I've ever met!

"OK," Lizzy agreed. "How about asking some other adults to coach too?"

"Sure," I said. "We could ask Grandpa's friend Tom, who used to work at LIGO, the Laser Interferometer Gravitational-Wave Observatory. He could add lots of brain power."

"Good idea," she agreed. "Here's what we should do. Let's organize a *Room Communication App* meeting with the kids this evening to see if they all want to join the team. If they do, we can discuss which adults to invite as coaches."

Lizzy's mood went from being dark to remaining happy for the rest of the day. We played a game of Boggle and had a nice visit to Dad's dungeon. He was happy to see us and hear all about the contest.

At 7:00 p.m., we logged in to the *Room Communication App*.

Lizzy sent out email invitations for a seven-thirty meeting. We invited our former *Cosmic Kids* teammates, our cousins VC and Milo, plus Jackson, Johari, and my friend Richie. Everyone showed up on the screen right on time.

"Hey, Jackson," said Lizzy, "your background looks really pretty. Where are you?"

"I'm on the Caltech campus," he answered. "Cool, huh? My classes are online except for the labs. So I come to campus on lab days."

Not to be outdone by her brother, Johari was in a beautiful place too. "Hi guys," she called. "That's the Santa Monica pier in back of me. I just finished a long walk on the beach."

"Show-offs," I said. "We could have some beautiful scenes of Connecticut for backgrounds too, but it's dark here at this hour." They were three hours earlier in California.

"But hey, you get to see my famous sneaker collection," said Milo, standing like a dork in front of a lot of shoes. "I have over fifty pairs of vintage sneakers. It's the Mount Rushmore of sneakers."

"Ha, ha," said Lizzy. "If it's a choice between stinky sneakers and the California beach, I'll go with the beach."

"More like Mount Smellmore," added Richie, and everyone laughed, even Milo.

"Ok, everyone," I said, "let's get serious. Everyone who was in the *Science and the Future Contest* last year should have gotten a letter about the new contest. So everyone except Richie knows about *The Race to the Big Bang*, right?"

"I haven't seen it," said Jackson.

"Me neither," said VC.

"Well," Lizzy said taking over, "Time and Space, Inc. is sponsoring a new contest."

Then I told them about the contest race using the *Beamer Virtual World* website and who could be on the team. Everyone was super excited about the huge cash prize and college scholarships. "Our mom read something in the business news about TSI's campaign to promote *Beamer Virtual World* as a combined search engine and social media platform. The contest is for publicity, so they want to make a big splash with big prizes."

"So," Lizzy interjected, "Neddy and I thought this would be a great way to have some fun during the lockdown. We can meet each other in the *Beamer Virtual World* for the next four months. Combining the two top teams from the *Science and the Future Contest* will give us a huge advantage, and we can add some adult members as coaches. I am sure our grandpa, who has a PhD in physics, would love to help us, and I think we can get Grandpa's friend Tom, who works in the space field, to join us too."

"Who's in?" I asked, cutting Lizzy off.

"I am so in," Johari called out. "My school closed too, and I'm getting really bored. Jackson gets to get out of the house, but I am stuck, like, basically in jail."

"I'm in," added Milo. "My life is getting to be like the movie *Groundhog Day*. Every day I wake up, and it's the same day all over again. Nothing changes. I don't even know what day of the week it is anymore."

"I'm in too," said VC. "My problem is my little brother, Griffin. We are cooped up together, and he is driving me crazy. I'm basically in charge of his online education because my parents are so busy with work. So I have to be a student and a teacher. This will give me a break."

"I'd . . . I'd love to do it," said Richie, who had a slight stutter. "Thanks, Neddy, for inviting me."

"Jackson?" I asked hopefully. He was, after all, busy with college and getting to be out in the world sometimes.

"No way would I miss it," he said.

I was so happy. "Fantastic," I said, beaming.

"This is how the contest will be run," Lizzy explained. "Each team will have a ship, like the *Cosmic Egg* that our team used in the last contest. We will use that for virtual travel in space and time. It can change size too, from smaller than atoms to bigger than stars. We'll have to provide the ship with provisions like fuel, oxygen, water, and food to make the trip."

"I think it's going to be a scavenger hunt through space and time," I added. "And there are a bunch of missions that have to be completed."

"And this is cool," said Johari, who was reading the contest announcement. "We have to build a space station in the *Virtual World* for our team to use when we go back seven billion years."

"Right," I said. "That's the goal of the *Regionals* competition. First is the *Qualifying Round* where any team can compete. Entries have to be in by April twenty-fifth. The *Qualifying Round* winners will be announced on May fifteenth."

"What about our coaches?" I asked. "Is everyone OK with Grandpa and Tom?"

"I'm good with them," Jackson agreed. "But I have an addition who could really help us. I would like to add Helen Nelson. She's one of my professors at Caltech, and her specialty is cosmology, you know, the study of the universe."

"OK," Lizzy concluded. "Jackson, you go ahead and ask your professor. Neddy and I will ask Grandpa and Tom. I'll type up our team list and plans. Let's do another call this weekend."

"I have an idea," said VC. "What if we all start keeping journals so we can keep track of our work and also keep track of how we got ourselves through this difficult time in our lives?"

Everyone agreed, and we ended the meeting.

/ / / / /

As soon as we got off the phone, Lizzy started typing up the plans.

Планы Лиззи на конкурс. Члены команды будут оригинальной командой исследователей космоса, плюс Джексон и Джохари. Coache3s будут Дедушка, Том и, возможно, профессор Джексонов.

"Ha, ha, very funny, Neddy!" she screamed at me. "One of these days, I am going to commit sistericide, or at least break half the bones in your body. I just typed a whole paragraph before I realized that you had fiddled with my computer so no one except the *Brooklyn Bunch* can read it. How did you make it type Russian letters?"

"There is no such word as 'sistericide,'" I replied. "And breaking only half my bones is kinder than Mom's threat to break every bone in my body. Maybe you and Mom could team up."

She rolled her eyes.

"It was just a joke," I said. "Can't you take a joke? To answer your question, I installed a program that uses a Cyrillic font. It translates into Russian as you type. You can let Milo use it to send messages in Russian to the *Brooklyn Bunch* team."

Her mood right then reminded me of the endless bad mood she was in last year after the watermelon catastrophe. Both Lizzy and Milo were in Grandpa's science class. Grandpa had the class drop objects of different weights out the second-story window to show that all objects have the same acceleration due to gravity. It was the experiment that Galileo did at the Leaning Tower of Pisa.

Milo was going to drop a tennis ball, and Lizzy was going to drop a watermelon. As she was holding it out the window, a bee landed on it right near her nose, and she threw it away from herself instead of carefully dropping it into the box with pillows. It almost hit our principal, Dr. Evil, who had just walked out the door. It hit the pavement right in front of her, and she got covered in watermelon juice and pieces. Grandpa got fired that day, and Lizzy always felt it was her fault. They made up before the moon trip, but the pandemic had made Lizzy angry again. I just wanted her to snap out of it.

3

SVETLANA ON MY MIND

(AS TOLD BY MILO)

The beginning of my first year of high school was awesome. I made the JV lacrosse team, and I was doing well in my classes even though Lizzy was in three of them. Our old competition over who could get better grades on tests was back in play. I was trying extra hard to beat her. I can't stand her smug smile when she wins.

I had been seeing Svetlana Larapova from the *Brooklyn Bunch* team. Last year they had competed against my team, the *Cosmic Kids*, in the *Science and the Future Contest*. Svetlana now went to my school since her family had moved from Brooklyn to Connecticut. She was beautiful and smart and had a cute Russian accent. But mostly I loved talking to her. She was the smartest girl I had ever met, and if you'd met my cousins, you'd know that was saying something.

Sometimes Svetlana and I got together on weekends for ice cream or to hike. I really liked being with her. On top of everything else, she had a great sense of humor. Once she got her identical twin sister, Natasha, to pretend to be her when I visited. Natasha even got me to kiss her. But I already had my doubts, and after one kiss, I knew for sure they had tricked me. It wasn't the awesomest of jokes, but even I had to admit it was pretty funny.

Of course, my family getting to go to the moon was awesome. We assembled at the airport in California, and the crew of the *Cosmic Voyager* brought us aboard. The *Voyager* was mounted on top of a booster rocket. When we accelerated away from the ground, it felt like my whole face was getting stretched to the back of my head! After a few minutes, we were going fast enough to escape Earth's gravity, and we disconnected from the booster. Then we were weightless.

Neddy, of course, was in heaven. She had the biggest smile on her face, and it lasted all the way to the moon and back. To pass the time, Jackson played gin rummy with Lizzy. VC and G-ma read their books and G-pa took pictures. Johari played her guitar, and I had my nose plastered to the window, looking at Planet Earth getting smaller and smaller. I kept thinking about Svetlana and all that we would do when we came home. We had become really good friends, even though I liked her as more than a friend.

It took two days to reach the moon. We circled for a day, took loads of pictures and videos, and then headed back. We ate food from toothpaste tubes and some surprise Chinese dumplings that G-ma had smuggled aboard.

Our reentry into Earth's atmosphere was scary. Outside, I could see the wings of our ship getting red hot, but we made it safely back to the airport and landed. We had a great celebration dinner, and on New Year's Eve, we headed back to Connecticut. The trip was awesome!

I spent New Year's Day at home trying to get my mind, which was still on the moon trip, to join my body, which was back on Earth. Then school started again. Svetlana and I were chatting in school every day and meeting every weekend. Finally, one day, she said in her perfect Russian accent, "I want to be your girlfriend. Do you want to be my boyfriend?"

How could anyone look into those beautiful eyes and say no?

On top of that, I was also really looking forward to the lacrosse season. In February, we started practicing. I was psyched.

That's when things started to unravel. Our whole lacrosse season was canceled because of the coronavirus. Then a lot of other bad stuff happened. G-pa and my uncle got sick, my school closed, and lockdown in my house began. I can meet Svetlana outside for our hikes, but we have to stay six feet apart. It's such a bummer.

So when Neddy and Lizzy talked about a plan to enter the *Race to the Big Bang Contest*, I felt a lot better. Immediately, I wanted to ask Svetlana to join our team, but I knew that would mean getting the others to agree.

The new contest gave me an awesome idea. Svetlana and I could meet in the *Beamer Virtual World*, the website we used during the *Science and the Future Contest*. I arranged a *Virtual World* date for Saturday. At 9:00 a.m. we logged on to MissionKT.

We appeared in the game as avatars. We also chose a mission crew role. We could choose *Explorer*, *Scientist*, *Guardian*, or *Navigator*. Each role had its own tools, like the *Explorer* could take photos, and the *Scientist* could make clones of dinosaurs. We could make the clones into pets that would follow us around.

We spawned into the game, and the first thing we did was to teleport to the rock garden. We built

a bunch of sculptures by piling rocks on top of one another. We made one five-huge-rocks tall and got a screen shot, but when we added the sixth rock, it collapsed. No one got hurt. That's a joke because obviously it was *virtual*.

After that, we played a game of hide and seek. We picked an area with boundaries where one of us would hide.

"No fair peeking at the screen," Svetlana called as she went to find her hiding place. It took me a while, but I found her.

Next, I hid, and she found me right away. After that, I cheated and looked at the screen. I watched Svetlana hide behind a rock at the bottom of a cliff. I snuck up to the top of the cliff above her, taking a route so she wouldn't see me. Then I pounced on her from above, yelling, "Gotcha!"

Svetlana screamed through my headphones. "You are going to pay for that," she yelled, laughing. "I have a special Russian revenge in mind!"

Uh, oh, I thought. *I'm* in trouble.

That was the end of the hide-and-seek game.

Svetlana wanted to go find a Triceratops, her favorite dinosaurs. I knew that because she had made a pet out of a Triceratops clone during last year's contest.

Scene from the 4-player video game "MissionKT." **TheBeamer LLC**

So we went hunting for Triceratops. We found a group of them on a hill with an awesome view overlooking a waterfall and a marsh filled with Titanosaurs. We could see our space/time ship, the *Cosmic Egg,* hovering above one of the Titanosaurs. We switched crew roles, and I became the *Explorer,* and she became the *Scientist.* I took a picture of her with the Triceratops and one of the Triceratops alone. The user interface on our screen indicated the amount of carbon atom stardust in our bodies that were once in that one Triceratops.

"Hey, Svetlana," I said, "look at the number on the screen. Each of us has 3,660 trillion carbon atoms that were once in just one single Triceratops. Awesome, huh?"

"Yeah, Milo," she said, "that's amazing. Can you explain how I got such a huge number of carbon atoms in me from just one Triceratops?"

For the *Science and the Future Contest,* Svetlana's sister, Natasha, had figured out how we are made of the same stardust that was once in the body of a Triceratops. She said that she had never understood it. Luckily, I did.

"OK," I answered. "It's really simple. Here's how it works. The Triceratops exhales carbon dioxide molecules made from carbon in its body. In its lifetime, it breathes out trillions of carbon atoms in the form of carbon dioxide. That carbon goes into the atmosphere, plants, animals, oceans, soils, and ocean sediments. All of those Triceratops carbon atoms, divided by the total number of all the carbon atoms on Earth, would be the *Triceratops fraction.* Almost everything on Earth that has carbon atoms would have the *Triceratops fraction* of carbon atoms in it. Got that?"

"Yes," said Svetlana, "I understand. The atmosphere, oceans, plants, and animals would all have the *Triceratops fraction,* and there would be *fractions* for all the other animals too."

"Right," I continued, feeling pretty proud of myself. "When your body got carbon from eating food, you were eating the *Triceratops fraction,* so you have that same *Triceratops fraction* of carbon atoms in your body. So, the 3660 trillion is simply the *Triceratops fraction* times the <u>total number of carbon atoms</u> in your body. And the amount of inherited Triceratops carbon is so large because you have about seven thousand trillion trillion carbon atoms in your body."

"Thanks, Milo," Svetlana said. "You are soooooo smart."

I think my face got red when she said that, so I was glad she was not able to see the real me.

Svetlana launched her drone and made a Triceratops clone pet. It was kinda cute, and she named it Topsy. I decided to make one, too, and I called it Turvy. Get it? Topsy-Turvy. We continued to explore. Topsy and Turvy followed us. It became kind of a pain in the butt because they kept bumping into us, so we decided to ditch them by teleporting. They would be OK; they had each other. Meanwhile, we headed for the beach to continue our awesome date.

We collected horseshoe crabs and threw them in the water. Then we played a game of catch. Svetlana would throw one towards me, and I would try to catch it with a *grab* tool.

It wasn't easy. I went one for twenty. Svetlana went one for three, and we quit. I liked that she showed me up. I thought it made her even cuter.

"Hey, Milo," Svetlana suggested, "let's go into the ocean and see if we can find some turtles. I love turtles."

We put on our helmets and explored the beautiful sea bottom and found a group of turtles who lived during the same era as the dinosaurs.

"Svetlana," I said through our head mikes, "change your role to the *Explorer* so you can take pictures. See if you can get a good one of me with a turtle."

Scenes from "The Stardust Mystery Online - Introduction." The STARDUST MYSTERY YouTube channel

Just then, one swam right past me. "I got it," she yelled. And then a shark swam past. I definitely freaked a little bit. "I got that too," Svetlana said, laughing. "You should have seen the look on your face."

After that, I had had enough sharks for one day, so we went back onto the beach. And guess who were there? Topsy and Turvy tracked us down.

Scene from the 4-player video game "MissionKT." TheBeamer LLC

"Where to now?" I asked. At the same time, we both pointed at the volcano. We switched to our *Teleport* tools and left the pets behind again.

The view from the top of the volcano was awesome. We could see the waterfall and the ocean beyond the mountains. There were a bunch of Pteranodons flying around that we could see in the distance. What a beautiful place to be, even if it was just virtual. Much better than being cooped up in the house.

Scene from the 4-player video game "MissionKT." **TheBeamer LLC**

I went over to Svetlana, and we rubbed virtual noses. Better than being six feet apart, I thought.

After we logged off, I decided that that was the most awesome date I'd ever been on. I started thinking about all the time I would be spending with my team and not with Svetlana. I definitely needed to do something about that. I had to get Svetlana on our team.

4

COSMIC EXPLORERS

(AS TOLD BY JACKSON)

The pandemic had made life better for me in school. As a fourteen-year-old kid attending college at Caltech, I always felt isolated. All the older kids had their groups, and I was pretty much always alone. But with the pandemic lockdown, everyone had to go it alone.

Meanwhile, the temperature in California was going up. We had a 101-degree day today, and our air conditioner stopped working. Dad got a repairman in, but we needed a whole new system. With our dad getting furloughed without pay from his job at the Getty Museum, it would not be getting fixed anytime soon. Pandemic problems!

I loved the idea of being on another team in another contest. Johari and I had become good friends with the *Cosmic Kids*. Lizzy and I were extra close. We always played gin rummy when we got together, and she usually beat me. I don't lose at too many things, so it made me pretty mad. But it also gave me a goal to focus on: beating Lizzy in gin rummy.

After our first team meeting, I went to see Professor Nelson in her office. The door was open, and she was working at her desk. I stayed by the door while she put on her mask.

"Hello, Jackson," she said through a mask covered in hundreds of numbers that make up the beginning of the number for Pi. "It is a pleasure to see my youngest student ever. What brings you to campus during lockdown?"

I walked in and sat down once we were both wearing our masks.

"I had to come in for my physics lab, and I wanted to ask you a question," I answered. Then I saw a picture on the wall behind her desk. "What is that?" I asked.

"That's Caltech's <u>Submillimeter Observatory</u> in Hawaii," she said. "It's on top of the Mauna Kea volcano on the Big Island. I worked there several years ago, but now it is being taken down." She explained that it was once used to get chemical compositions in gas clouds in outer space. It also

provided information on galaxy formation. "We even saw light from a galaxy that was emitted twelve billion years ago," she said excitedly.

"What a rad place to work," I said. "But is it safe? Don't volcanoes erupt?"

"Well, Mauna Kea is pretty stable," she answered. "But some of the other volcanoes on the island do erupt periodically. It is quite a sight to see. So what is it you wanted to ask me?"

I explained to Professor Nelson all about *The Race to the Big Bang Contest* and told her about the rest of our team, including the two possible physicist coaches, Grandpa and Tom.

"For the first part of the *Race*," I started, "we have to build a space station that we can use as we time travel and complete missions. Then there are some cosmic scavenger hunts."

She nodded, interested, so I continued. "We need you to coach us, especially for the scavenger hunts. It's a search for special, unusual objects in the universe. You can really help us with that. There will be one remote, one-hour brainstorming meeting a week with all the team members. What do you say? Will you join our team?"

"Let me think about it," she said.

"Oh, wait," I added. "The grand prize is one million dollars in cash and up to one million dollars in college scholarships. The *Regionals* winner gets $25,000, and the contest is only four months long. It will be over by the end of August."

"I'm in," she said, smiling. That was all it took. A little financial motivation could go a long way during the uncertainty of a pandemic. Just ask my dad.

"Oh rad," I said. "Our next *Room App* team meeting is next week. We'll send you an invitation."

◢ ◢ ◢ ◢ ◢

I called Lizzy to tell her my news.

"Doctor Nelson is in. What about G-pa and Tom?"

"Grandpa is in," said Lizzy. "Neddy and I rode down to the hospital again to ask him. We stood outside and used my phone to talk. We told him all about the contest and asked him to be our coach. Since he had already been our coach for the *Science and the Future Contest*, he immediately agreed."

"What about his friend Tom?" I asked.

"Grandpa said he would ask Tom, but he was sure he would join us too. And there is good family news," Lizzy continued. "Grandpa is feeling a lot better and will be home in two days. He told us that he was lucky because people his age were sicker longer and sometimes even died of the virus. Our dad is doing better too."

"Great," I said. "Let's set up a *Room* meeting for next Saturday at two." Then I texted Professor Nelson's email address to Neddy and Lizzy so they could invite her.

◢ ◢ ◢ ◢ ◢

Neddy and Lizzy started the meeting at one-thirty. I signed on early so the three of us could talk about what we needed to do to get started. Having this many people on one team meant we'd have to stay really organized. I offered to fill out the entry form.

"We have to pick a name for our team," said Lizzy.

"And we have to submit a team picture with the application," offered Neddy.

"We have to create a set of tasks and a schedule," I added.

By 2:05, everyone had been admitted to the *Room* meeting.

We debated the question of a name. After half an hour of heated discussion, mostly among us kids, we settled on the *Cosmic Explorers*.

VC asked everyone for head shots to make our team picture. Then we discussed tasks and scheduling. It was decided that mainly the kids would use the *Beamer Virtual World*. The coaches could join when we needed them. We would have a meeting with the whole team once a week to report to the adults, make plans, and get the coaches' feedback.

Grandpa reminded us to call him if we needed his input in between meetings. Professor Nelson, who told us all to use her first name, Helen, said the same.

"Hey, everyone," said VC, "take a look at this."

She shared her screen to show us the team picture that she had quickly assembled.

Everyone agreed that the picture looked great. I was pretty good at graphic design, but VC was truly next level.

Our first task for the contest was to qualify for the *Regionals*. Then, for the *Regionals*, we would have to design and build the space station. We were all most excited about that because it was for a prize of $25,000. Johari's and my percentage of that could come in really handy for our family.

The idea that we eventually adopted for our space station came from the most unexpected source: Richie, the youngest member of the team. He said, "I have kinda an unusual idea for our space station. Let me put a plan together, and I will tell you about it at the next meeting."

I was more than a little curious about what it would be.

5

NEARLY NORMAL

(AS TOLD BY VC—VICTORIA CLAIR)

Starting on April first, school classes were being taught remotely. Most of the online classes were stinky boring. Plus being in lockdown with my little brother, Griffin, was torture. He was constantly bugging me to play with him or asking me crazy questions—not to mention the fact that my parents expected me to basically be his teacher while he was learning remotely. I mean I get that they are really busy with finding work and dealing with their restaurant being closed. I get that we all have to pull our own weight, but I was pulling my own weight plus Griffy's, and Griffy was pulling zero weight.

Wearing a mask is a pain, too, but I know it is important. With Mom and Dad out of work because their restaurant was closed, I was feeling bad.

But things started improving when the contest began. By the middle of April, Lizzy and Neddy's dad was out of the basement, and Papa, which is the name I call Grandpa, was out of the hospital.

My French class was the one online course that was good. I even won a medal from the French Honor Society. And, of course, we were all excited about the contest. It gave us something positive to fill the hours during this difficult time, and I loved being with our team. The prize money and college scholarships for winning the contest would surely help my family's financial situation.

To improve things further, Lizzy, Neddy, and I started inventing new activities that would bring our lives back to something more like normal. We called them pandemic pastimes. Then the whole family, including my mom and dad, Papa and Grandma, and the aunts, uncles, and cousins, started inventing pandemic pastimes too.

The first thing we did was to create a <u>family bubble</u>. My mom and dad were home trying to figure out how to earn some money. Milo's dad was working remotely from home. Lizzy and Neddy's mom and dad were professors at the University of Connecticut, which had closed, so they were staying home too. Papa and Grandma were at home, not seeing anyone either.

The adults decided to form a family bubble. We agreed on all the safety measures everyone would take so that we could all still get together. There would be no visits inside our houses by anyone except the bubble people. That would allow Milo and me to get together with Lizzy and Neddy in person for the contest meetings and *Virtual World* adventures.

Now that we could see each other, Milo and I went over to Lizzy and Neddy's house for a visit. We went into the family room, where Neddy and Lizzy were watching TV. Milo didn't even say hello. He just blurted out, "I would like to ask Svetlana to join our team."

21

I had a hunch that was coming. Since last summer, Milo has had a giant crush on her. But I didn't think she would ditch her sisters and brother if their family decided to enter the contest. "I'll check with the rest of our team to see if anyone objects to inviting Svetlana," I said.

I checked, and by the next day, I told him that no one objected to Svetlana joining us. I actually really liked her. She was smart and, like me, great at languages.

The next pandemic activity was art. All us kids took a virtual art class together. Our great-aunt, Papa's sister, had started teaching remote art classes using the *Room App*. It was for all the kids in the family. That included our second cousins, her grand-kids. So every Monday evening, we all logged into *Room* and did art projects.

Grandma saw how well this worked, so Wednesday became online cooking class. We made fried dumplings in our first meeting. Grandma had her computer connected to a *Room* meeting with the camera pointing first at the preparation area and then at the frying pan. Papa took a picture of the scene. I was at Lizzy and Neddy's house and we followed along. Our dumplings came out delicious.

We heard that outdoor activities were pretty safe. So, one day, we met Papa and Grandma for a picnic at Heublein Tower. It was a huge old mansion that is now open to the public. Papa dropped Grandma, Lizzy, Neddy, Milo, Griffin, and me at the trailhead. Then he drove up to the picnic area with the food.

It was a beautiful, sunny morning as we started up the trail. Grandma led the way, followed by Milo and me, with Lizzy, Griffin, and Neddy bringing up the rear. We hiked for about ten minutes up a very steep trail.

"I'm tired," whined Neddy. "This is too much work."

Grandma shot her a look and said, "if a seventy-five-year-old grandmother and a six-year-old boy can do this, a healthy twelve-year-old can do it too. Suck it up."

Lizzy and I laughed. Neddy's cheeks turned red, but she didn't complain anymore.

After another five minutes, we reached the top of the ridge. The view from there was

fantastic. We could see down into the valley for at least ten miles. It was definitely a photo op.

Grandma took a bunch of pictures of the view. Then she said, "OK, my sweet grandchildren, please line up for a picture." The older kids started posing at the edge of the cliff. "Hey, kids," Grandma yelled, "be careful. Come away from the edge. It's more than a hundred-foot drop."

After the pictures, we continued up the trail. Then something exciting and scary happened. I had taken the lead, way ahead of the rest of the gang. What I saw in the woods made me turn around and run like crazy.

"A bear!" I screamed. "Run!"

Sure enough, a big black bear came lumbering out of the woods onto the trail. It was about twenty feet away. Grandma shushed us and told us to freeze. If it wanted to, the bear could have definitely hurt us. Lizzy grabbed her phone and started shooting pictures.

Thankfully, the bear gave us humans a quick look and then proceeded across the trail into the woods on the other side. Milo and Neddy, who were holding their breath, both let out a huge sigh and looked like they were going to crumple to the ground. Grandma was holding Griffin in her arms.

"How come you weren't scared?" I asked Lizzy. "Bears can be really dangerous. You just stood there calmly taking pictures. You can't outrun a bear."

"It isn't like I have to outrun the bear," replied Lizzy. "I just have to outrun *one of you*."

Later, Lizzy showed everyone her best picture of the bear. She said, "Grandpa is gonna love this one."

Which brings me to the next pandemic pastime. Besides getting exercise outdoors, Papa had started offering us a twenty-dollar prize every month to the grandchild who took the best wildlife photograph. He knew by then that we were really motivated by prizes! That month, Milo and I were neck and neck. I had a lovely picture of three deer in the woods, and Milo had some great shots of a mother turkey with four babies. But everyone agreed that the bear shot would probably be the winner that month.

A short time later, after a final uphill climb, we reached the Heublein Tower. Papa was there with the lunch laid out on a picnic table. We had turkey sandwiches with tomatoes and apple juice to drink.

After lunch, we explored the Heublein house and climbed to the room on the fifth floor, with views in all directions.

"This view is super cool," squealed Neddy. "You can see for miles. I can see all the buildings in Hartford and the hospital in Farmington. I can even see our house."

After the tour, we went back down and outside. Grandma asked a fellow hiker to take a photo of our group. Then it was time to go home.

"Hey, Milo," I asked as we started our hike down from the tower, "where did you get the pictures of the turkeys? I have seen wild turkeys before, but I have never seen turkey babies."

"They were in Westmore Park," he answered. "I was walking with Svetlana when we saw them. And don't worry—we were six feet apart."

"Did you say anything to her about joining the team?" I asked.

"Not gonna happen," he replied. "She and her siblings got letters from TSI too. So, they are forming a team of their own to compete in the contest. She said her family would disown her if she joined our team."

"OK," I said, "then our team is finalized."

Neddy told me about another new pandemic pastime. Jackson had programmed an online gin rummy game so that he could continue playing remotely with Lizzy. I guess he was determined to finally win a game against her. She downloaded his application, and they played. Neddy said that it worked great. It dealt the cards randomly and showed each of the player's cards on the screen. It randomly provided new cards as they picked and discarded. Neddy said that Lizzy is continuing to win. Poor *Boy Genius* is not the smartest one at everything.

That night, we had a *Cosmic Explorer* team meeting to go over our entry form. Jackson made the changes that the team suggested. He added the street addresses and email addresses for all the team members so everyone would get the notices. I made a final copy of the team picture. We all checked over the entry form, and then Jackson pressed the submit button. We were ready to start *The Race to the Big Bang*.

PART 2
THE QUALIFYING ROUND
(EARLY MAY)

QUALIFYING BEGINS

(AS TOLD BY JOHARI)

My twin brother, Jackson, and I live with our parents near the ocean in Santa Monica, California. I always loved that we lived so close to the beach. I got to go running, biking, and swimming. But Jack has always been kinda hard to live with because he is so good at everything. He competed with me in school and in sports, but he won the school competition by a landslide when he got into college at just thirteen years old. Honestly, that made life better for me because he went away to college. But with the pandemic, he was back home again and commuting to campus only on lab days.

Jackson and I met Lizzy and the other *Cosmic Kids* in California last year during the *Science and the Future Contest*. We won the *Finals*, they came in second, and we went on the moon trip together. It made me pretty happy that Lizzy beats my brother at gin rummy all the time. He needs a good lesson in humility. He even created an online gin rummy game to try evening up the score with her. It isn't happening.

Lizzy was helpful when lockdown began, sharing all their family's ideas for pandemic pastimes with me. I was already hiking and biking on the boardwalk. Lizzy's grandpa let me join their photo contest, but we don't have any deer, turkeys, or bears around here. Maybe I could spot a whale. I also joined her grandma's Wednesday cooking classes.

Jackson came up with a new activity. He started juggling. Our dad took a picture of him juggling three balls on the beach near the Santa Monica pier. That's me in the background watching. I made the picture into my wallpaper because I thought it was cool.

In the *Science and the Future Contest*, Jackson and I were the only two people on our team. We actually managed to work together really well and ultimately won the contest.

Jackson knew right away that stardust was atoms as soon as we got our first clue. Atoms are what our bodies and all physical things in our world are made of. Atoms are incredibly tiny, and we have more than a billion, billion, billion of them in each of our bodies. That's a one followed by twenty-seven zeros. Hydrogen and helium, the smallest atoms, were created in the Big Bang. All the larger atoms were formed in the centers of stars and in star supernova explosions that occur at the end of their lives. That's why the atoms we were looking for are called *stardust*. In the incredible heat of those explosions, the little atoms merge together by nuclear fusion to form the bigger ones. The smaller atoms like carbon, oxygen, and nitrogen were formed by supernovas from first-generation gas stars. That happened just two to three hundred million years after the *Big Bang*. That was really soon after the *Big Bang* in the scheme of time, even though it sounds like a big number. The biggest atoms weren't formed until five billion years later, when the second-generation stars burned out and had their supernova explosions. Jackson was also surprised to find out about the quadrillion tons of gold and other atoms formed in a neutron star pair merger. I still felt pretty smug about having told him about that.

The contest was the *Greatest Of All Time*, the GOAT. When Jackson and I won first place, we couldn't believe it. We were so excited when Lizzy, VC, Neddy, and Milo got to come on the trip to the moon too. The moon trip with them was incredible. The six of us became even better friends. So Jackson and I were really psyched when they asked us to join them for the new contest.

The *Cosmic Kids* kept a journal during the last contest. VC's dad helped them make it into an illustrated storybook called The Stardust Mystery. This time around, we were all contributing to another journal. I hoped we could make *this* journal into a book too.

On May 1, we all got the same letter from TSI saying that our application was accepted, and they gave us a schedule for the contest. We had fifteen days to qualify.

The letter was signed by Quentin Quixote, known as Dr. Q, and his sister Quinna. Lizzy told me that Dr. Q and Grandpa went to graduate school together, and he met Quinna when they both worked at NASA. Apparently, there was a huge feud between Dr. Q and his sister. They hadn't talked to each other in years. But the feud got patched up at the end of the *Science and the Future Contest*. It was nice to see that they were now working together, and she was getting credit for the work she did that helped launch TSI. When they made up, Dr. Q actually made her president of the company. I guess sisters and brothers can get along sometimes. Maybe there is hope for Jackson and me.

We logged on to *Room* for our team meeting and discussed all the contest rules and the schedule. Then we quit *Room*, and just the kids logged on to the *Beamer Virtual World*. We were going to do the activities that TSI had created to introduce the contest rules and the *Qualifying* round missions. The adults figured we kids could handle the *Beamer* on our own. Among the six of us, we had all the top scorers from the last contest.

May 1, 2020

Dear Team Cosmic Voyagers,

Time and Space Inc. is pleased to accept your application to compete in our *Race to the Big Bang* competition. Your team will be one of 49 teams competing in the New England region *Qualifying* round. Only the twenty top-scoring teams will qualify for the *Regionals* competition with a cash prize of $25,000. The three top teams in each region will be eligible to compete in the *Finals* for the grand prizes of $100,000, $250,000 and $1,000,000 in cash and up to $1,000,000 in college scholarships.

All the rules for the contest are enclosed. The schedule is as follows:

Qualifying round: May 1 to May 15 – Teams will be judged for qualifying based on their performance in the following Virtual World sessions – Virtual Trip to the Moon; Peculiar things in the Solar System; Peculiar Things in the Ocean; and Saving the Big Bang. Screen time spent in the *Qualifying* round will not count for the *Regionals and Finals*.
The *Regionals*: May 16 to June 30 - Building your Space Station.
The *Finals*: July 15 to August 30 - Finding cosmic objects and building the first atoms in the universe.

We wish you the best of luck.

Sincerely,

Qu Qu and **Q Q**

Quentin Quixote, CEO, and Quinna Quixote, President
Time and Space, Inc.

Time & Space, Inc, 33 Navaho Blvd, Palo Alto, CA 13456,   555 432 1234

The *Virtual World* was set up for the contest introduction. We chose our avatars and pressed "READY," and our avatars spawned into the scene outside a building which we knew from the previous contest was the *Mystery Museum*. We raced our avatars up the stairs to the entrance and went inside.

The *Mystery Museum* was the place where we would teleport to the *Cosmic Egg*, our travel ship that allowed us to experience any place, time, space, or size-change. But now there was new stuff important to *this* contest. We split up and started to explore.

"Hey, everybody," announced Neddy, who had teamed up with Richie. "We found a large meeting room with a sign out front that says 'Race to the Big Bang Introduction.' Inside there are some big computer screens. I betcha that is where we need to go."

"Gotcha," called Lizzy, who was with me and VC. We all headed for the room along with Milo and Jackson.

Just as Neddy said, there were three large screens with computer monitors inside. "Look guys," I said. "Each one has a different subject about the race."

"Let's split up again and investigate in teams," suggested Jackson. "Then we can meet and discuss what we learned. I'd like to tackle the MISSIONS."

"Good idea," I agreed. "I'll do the SPECIAL EQUIPMENT."

"I'll go with Johari," Neddy said excitedly. Richie, of course, stuck with Neddy.

"I'll go with *Boy Genius* on MISSIONS," added VC as she snuggled up to him. We all chuckled.

"OK," I summarized, "that leaves Lizzy and Milo to find out about PROVISIONS." Knowing that they sometimes didn't get along so well, I asked, "Are you two good with that?"

"Sweet," Milo said with a smirk on his face. Lizzy just nodded.

We spent two hours in the meeting room doing our research. While we were there, I noticed two people quietly come into the room. They stayed in the background, observing what we were doing.

Neddy whispered in my ear, "That's Svetlana and her sister, Natasha. What are they doing here?"

I shrugged.

By the time we were finished doing our research, they were gone. We assembled our avatars by the giant window with the view of the mountains to discuss what we had learned.

"Did you guys see Svetlana and Natasha come in before?" I asked. "I think they were spying on us."

Nobody else had noticed them. Milo suggested that we were hallucinating.

"I am sure they were there. Neddy and I both saw them," I argued. "This is serious. With over a million dollars at stake here, we need to keep our team's progress totally secret if we are going to win. The prizes are really important for Jackson and me now that our dad is not working."

"Me too," said VC. "Our restaurant is still closed. Dad is working at another restaurant, but I'm worried that he'll come down with the virus."

"Winning is really important to Neddy and me too," added Lizzy, "since our parents are not working either."

"Milo, don't talk to Svetlana about our progress," I warned.

"I would never do that," he objected.

"OK, team," said Lizzy, getting us back on track, "what did we learn?"

Milo started us off. "Here is the deal with PROVISIONS," he began. "For each trip back in time, you need to have provisions. That is fuel for the *Cosmic Egg*, oxygen for us to breathe, water to drink, and food to eat."

"Right," added Lizzy. "And how much you need depends on your screen time. The more screen time you use, the more the provisions are consumed."

"So," explained Milo, "if you do a short time or space travel trip, you use very little fuel, oxygen, water, and food. Do a long trip, and you use a lot. You have to be careful about what you do."

"Now," Lizzy continued, "where do we get provisions? We can collect provisions wherever we can find them. For example, we can fill our tanks with oxygen from the Earth's atmosphere and water from the Earth's lakes."

"And there is a second way to get provisions," Milo added. "We can buy them and have them delivered to wherever we are in time and space. But that costs something called *currency*."

Milo and Lizzy were presenting as a great tag team, I thought. "So what is *currency*, and how do we get it?" I asked.

"Good questions," Milo replied. "*Currency* consists of precious things like gold, diamonds, and other gems. We have to find it on our travels. One more thing: at the end of our presentation, there was a warning that said to be prepared to deal with something unexpected."

"Milo and I were both wondering what that might be," said Lizzy.

"Hey guys," I said, "looking for *currency* explains one of the tools listed in SPECIAL EQUIPMENT." Now my team took over the presentation. "Richie, do you want to tell them about the metal detector?"

"Yes," he answered, "I tested one of them. It will give a signal when any metal, such as gold or iron, is under the detector. There is also a setting to detect crystals like diamonds."

"Thanks, Richie," I said. "There is one other piece of SPECIAL EQUIPMENT that I think could be very important. It's called the Multi-Messenger Astronomy system. The *Cosmic Egg* can be equipped with detectors for gravitational waves and radiation to identify events like supernovas and stuff."

"Like the system that identified the merger of neutron stars you told me about?" Jackson asked. I nodded. "Yep."

"Don't forget," Lizzy said taking over, "we have all the other measurement tools for composition, density, velocity, temperature, and mass that we used before in the *Virtual World*."

"So, Jack and VC," I asked, "what about the MISSIONS?"

"Let's go look at the picture at the back of the room," said Jack. "That will help explain some of the MISSIONS. The picture shows the history of the universe as if all 13.8 billion years happened in just one hour. On that scale, the Earth formed twenty minutes ago, the dinosaurs became extinct twenty seconds ago, and we *Homo Sapiens* arrived just 0.1 second ago. Two of our missions are to find an early event that produced our lightest atoms and one that produced our heaviest atoms."

"And," added VC, "we have to build the first atoms of hydrogen and helium starting from Quarks and electrons produced in the first second of the *Big Bang*. There are also some peculiar objects for us to find in time and space."

"Think about this guys," added Jackson. "All the physical things in the universe are made of just quarks and electrons in different arrangements. Incredible, right?"

"This is the mission I like best," continued VC. "We have to measure the distance from Earth to the Andromeda galaxy as we go back in time. The idea is to show that the universe has been expanding since the Big Bang. Since *Andromeda* was formed ten billion years ago, we get the expansion information for a big part of the existence of our 13.8-billion-year-old universe."

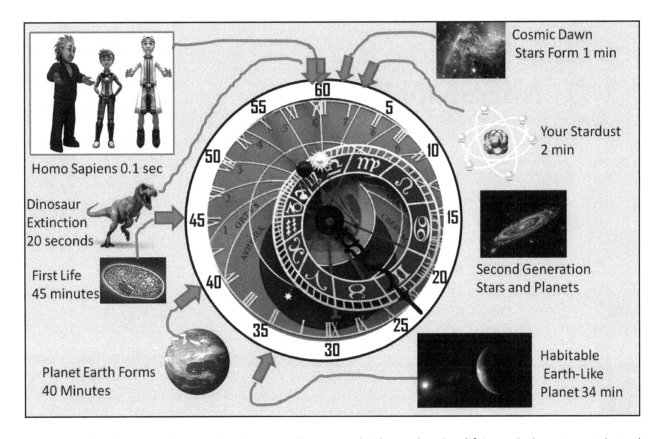

Cosmic Dawn
Stars Form 1 min

Your Stardust
2 min

Homo Sapiens 0.1 sec

Dinosaur
Extinction
20 seconds

Second Generation
Stars and Planets

First Life
45 minutes

Planet Earth Forms
40 Minutes

Habitable
Earth-Like
Planet 34 min

"So," said Milo summing up, "we have to do a good job on the *Qualifying* missions to get into the *Regionals*. Then we have to design one of the best space stations to advance from the *Regionals* to the *Finals*. Then we have to accomplish all of the missions and finally reach the *Big Bang* and build hydrogen and helium. And to win the contest, we have to complete the *Regionals* and *Finals* using the least amount of screen time."

"That means," Lizzy added, "we have to plan each *Virtual World* session carefully. We have to make sure that we have enough provisions, and we have to keep our screen time as low as possible. If we are going to win all the money we'll need for college, everyone has to know about all the tools and equipment we can use to do all the missions and overcome any obstacles."

"There are also some other training missions available," I added. "You should do them if you need more practice using the tools."

7

MISSION KT

(AS TOLD BY NEDDY)

Life is definitely improving. I am so glad to see Dad doing normal stuff in the house like having dinner with us instead of being quarantined in the basement. And Lizzy's mood is way better too. But that also means she is up to fighting with me for the TV remote instead of lying in her bed. I guess that's better than the mopey Lizzy.

Lately I'd been practicing for the contest with Mission KT. It takes place sixty-five million years ago, just before an asteroid hit Planet Earth and wiped out all the land dinosaurs. It uses the same crew roles (*Explorer, Scientist, Guardian,* and *Navigator*) that the contest uses, and each crew role has special instruments and capabilities.

There are instruments to measure temperature, chemical composition, velocity, density, and mass of objects in the *Virtual World*. The *Explorer* could take photographs, the *Scientist* could make small clone pets of the dinosaurs, and the *Guardian* could time-freeze things. Everyone could get information on things and pick up objects and move them around.

The *Guardian* could even make dinosaurs do things like lie down in the river to make a bridge for us. The *Navigator* could look down from the *Cosmic Egg* ship and place beacons on the ground to tell the rest of the crew where to go to find things. *Mission KT* is a really beautiful and fun *Virtual World*.

But the whole team except for Richie had already been there and done that. So, we all decided that Richie would do *Mission KT* with me alone. We'd practice some of the tools we would need for the contest to bring him up to speed.

Richie and I have known each other since first grade. He is a great artist and has been doing some of the illustrations for our journal. But in elementary school, Richie was my worst nightmare. He teased me constantly about my habit of sometimes daydreaming. He called me mean names like Space Cadet, Loony Probe, and Cosmic Cuckoo. One day when I accidently came to school with toilet paper stuck in my hair, he had the whole class calling me Hairy Potty. I know that was kind of funny, but it was still mean!

Then one day there was this incident on the school playground. He was teasing me, and I ran away crying. Lizzy saw what was happening and threatened to really hurt him if he didn't stop bullying me. Richie pushed her, and she responded with her martial arts, a flying double kick that came within an inch of his nose. He fell on his butt. They both got detentions and had to write essays. Richie had to apologize to me for his bullying. He confessed that he really liked me. He said that he was jealous that I was so smart, and that he thought I was the coolest girl in the whole class. He stopped being mean, and now we are even good friends.

As we logged in to *Mission KT*, we used our headsets to talk. We each chose our avatars and I explained to Richie about the different crew roles. Richie liked the idea of taking photographs, so he chose the *Explorer*. I chose the *Guardian*. We clicked *"Ready"* and then *"Start Game."*

Our avatars spawned into the *Virtual World*. Then we followed the path in front of us that led to the top of a hill. It overlooked a beautiful valley where a herd of dinosaurs roamed.

"Wow," yelled Richie, "this is beautiful. I love the volcano. Can I take a picture?"

Scenes from the 4-player video game "MissionKT." **TheBeamer LLC**

"Just left click your mouse," I answered. "You started the game with the *Photo* tool. If you click the tab key, you can see your photos in the *Virtual World Journal.*"

"Cool," said Richie. "I'm going to make an album of pictures from this mission."

"Good idea," I responded. "Now let's go find a T-Rex." I showed Richie how to choose the *Teleport* tool and told him to go to location number four.

I knew exactly what I was doing. I knew where we would find a T-Rex. This was going to be perfect. I led Richie down the hill and through the trees. When we came out into the clearing, there was a huge T-Rex right in front of him. It looked at Richie, opened its mouth, and let out a huge roar.

Richie was so scared that he let out a yell, and I heard a real-life crash over the headset that I think was his chair getting knocked over.

"I am so out of here," he screamed. Seconds later, his avatar disappeared.

"You idiot," I said, calling him up on his cell phone. "You didn't have to shut down to get away from the T-Rex. Did you think it was going to jump off the screen into your room? Now we have to log in again. But that was a little payback for all your years of teasing me."

"Hey," he said sheepishly, "I just totally freaked out."

So, we logged back on and went back to the T-Rex.

*Scenes from the 4-player video game "MissionKT." **TheBeamer LLC***

I showed Richie how to switch to *Scientist* and measure the T-Rex's elemental composition.

"Hey Neddy," he said, "look at the screen. The T-Rex has carbon, hydrogen, oxygen, and nitrogen just like a human. And the bar charts with the percentages of each element show that humans have about the same amounts of carbon, hydrogen, oxygen, and nitrogen as dinosaurs."

"Well, all animals have pretty much the same elemental compositions," I said. Then Richie used his *Information* tool to discover that each of us has inherited over five thousand trillion carbon atoms that were once in just that one T-Rex.

*Scene from the 4-player video game "MissionKT." **TheBeamer LLC***

"That's so hard to believe," he said. I agreed, but I already knew all of this from *The Stardust Mystery*. My mind had been blown months ago.

"Hey, Richie," I yelled, "let's switch roles, and I will show you something really cool." As the *Scientist*, I turned on my *Launch Drone* tool. I piloted the drone through the three blue circles on top of the T-Rex to make a miniature clone pet, which I named *Rexy*.

"I wanna make a clone pet too," said Richie.

"OK," I agreed, "but let's find a different dinosaur." So, we started exploring again.

"How about a Triceratops clone?" Richie asked pointing to a bunch of them on a hill.

First Richie, and then I, successfully made Triceratops clone pets. Then Richie saw some Titanosaurs down in the marsh near a waterfall and made a clone pet of one of them too.

Scenes from the 4-player video game "MissionKT." **TheBeamer LLC**

The four pets followed us around. *Rexy* was always in the lead, followed by the Titanosaur that Richie named *Titan*. The two Triceratops pets, *Cera* and *Topsy*, were way in the rear.

"Can I take some more pictures?" asked Richie. "The artist in me loves it here." We explored, and Richie shot pictures. He got a great one of the river with the volcano in the background and Pterano-dons flying above. There was even a T-Rex in the lower left.

Scene from the 4-player video game "MissionKT." **TheBeamer LLC**

"Hey, Richie," I said, "I'll show you something you're gonna love. Switch roles to *Navigator*, choose the *Beacon* tool, and then left click."

"Wow, this is cool," Richie yelled. "Where am I?"

"You are in the *Cosmic Egg* ship," I answered. "It is hovering above us. Left click, and you can put down some marker beacons at the spot that you point at. Mark a trail to the top of the volcano."

"Hey, Neddy, look at this beautiful scene I got with the beacon trail up the volcano and the Pteranodons flying toward me."

Scene from the 4-player video game "MissionKT." **TheBeamer LLC**

"Awesome," I agreed. "Now let's go up to the top of the volcano."

When we got to the top, I showed Richie how to measure the temperature of the lava and the velocity of the asteroid that was heading for Earth. It was an asteroid that scientists believe wiped out the dinosaurs.

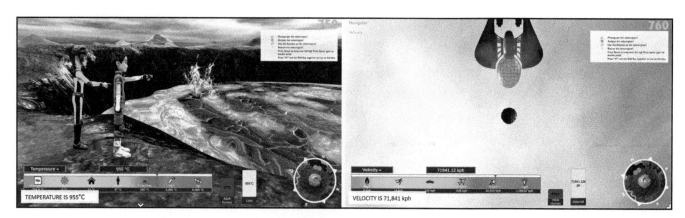

Scenes from the 4-player video game "MissionKT." **TheBeamer LLC**

Richie was starting to get bored with all the measurements I was making him take, so I let him off the hook to go take pictures for a while.

We explored as Richie filled the *Journal* with pictures. One of my favorites was of two Titanosaurs near the waterfall.

Scene from the 4-player video game "MissionKT." **TheBeamer LLC**

"While we are here," I said, "let me show you one more thing. I'll switch to *Guardian*, you switch to *Explorer*, and you can photograph what I do. Follow me."

I led us away from the waterfall to where there was a Titanosaurus standing in the river. "I'm switching to the *Animate* tool," I said as I zapped the dinosaur.

"Cool," said Richie. "It's lying down in the river."

"Now I'm switching to the *Time Freeze* tool." I zapped the Titanosaurus as it was lying down, and it froze in place. "OK, Richie, let's cross over my bridge."

Scenes from the 4-player video game "MissionKT." **TheBeamer LLC**

"I led Richie to the beach and the rock garden. Then I said, "I think I showed you all you need to know. Go ahead and explore. Take all the pictures you want and then log off."

We finished our visit before the asteroid hit the Earth.

8

VIRTUAL TRIP TO THE MOON

(AS TOLD BY JACKSON)

I am really psyched about the contest, but the news from California is not great. One of the kids in my lab got Covid, so now all the kids in that class are quarantined for fourteen days. So, I am home full time with Johari. The temperature is still topping the hundred degree mark most days, and Johari is driving me batty. She is either complaining about her boring online classes, or she is singing. Yeah, she has decided she is going to be a singer, and Mom is encouraging her and even got her a coach that she visits online. She has always been the favorite child. I am really thankful for the contest distraction.

All of the *Cosmic Explorer* kids are going to do the *Virtual Trip to the Moon*. Grandpa is going to come too. The objective of this mission is to travel to the moon and find out what it is like. We have to measure the size, weight, acceleration of gravity, density, temperature, and composition of the atmosphere and land. We have to submit a report on our mission that will be used to determine if we get into the *Regionals*.

I'm not bragging, but I already know this task will be pretty easy. I did most of those calculations with Neddy out of curiosity, while we were on our actual trip to the moon. It was great to have a fellow nerd to hang out with.

We started our mission at 9:00 a.m. my time, which was twelve noon for everyone on the East coast. We all logged in to the *Virtual World*, went to the *Mystery Museum*, and teleported to the *Cosmic Egg*.

The kids agreed that I would be the leader for this mission. "OK, who picked the role of *Navigator*?" I asked the crew.

"That's me," answered Lizzy.

"You have to program your computer to take us to the moon," I instructed her.

"Aye, aye, sir," she agreed with a dramatic salute. "I'm on it."

Soon, we were on our way. At some point, Richie asked us all, very seriously, "Did you guys hear about the bones they found on the moon?" After a pause he answered, "The cow didn't jump high enough." Then he burst into annoying laughter.

It brought groans from the rest of us, and unfortunately the moon jokes kept coming.

"What holds up the moon?" Neddy asked.

"Moonbeams," answered Lizzy.

"How do you know when the moon is going broke?" asked Milo. Without waiting for an answer, he said, "When it's down to its last quarter."

Even Grandpa contributed. "Did you hear about the new restaurant on the moon? The food is great, but there's no atmosphere."

Thankfully, we arrived at the moon before anyone else could add their two cents. Virtual travel is much faster than real travel, so we were there in less than ten minutes instead of the two days for the real trip. The actual travel time was less than one second. It took five minutes to speed up and five to slow down. I was using virtual-reality goggles instead of my computer screen. As I looked out at the vast blackness of empty space, it seemed like a very lonely place to be. Our beautiful planet is like a lively theme park in that lonely space.

We had one problem. All the clone pets that Neddy and Richie had created apparently continue to follow their creators all over

the *Virtual World*. It turned out that Milo had one also. It was from a date he went on with Svetlana in *Mission KT*. So, they were all there with us on our trip to the moon. We had three miniature Triceratops, a Titanosaurus, and a T-Rex. They were cute, but just like Milo and Svetlana discovered, they are pains in the butt. They keep bumping into us. So, we locked them in the utility room. Neddy's T-Rex pet,

Rexy, and another dinosaur named Topsy didn't like that. They made a terrible racket. We let them out to hang with us in the main cabin. We'll ditch them when we teleport to the surface of the moon.

"Hey, kids," asked Grandpa, "do you mind if we go back in time? I was at NASA when they took the famous picture of Astronaut David Scott saluting the American flag. I would like to be on the moon to see that."

Everyone thought that was a cool idea, so we went back to the date Grandpa wanted: August 1, 1971.

"Let's make some circles around the moon like we did on our real voyage," I suggested when we got close. "We can look for the NASA landing site, and our *Navigator* can measure the moon's circumference." The most disappointing thing about our real trip was that we just circled and didn't get to go to the surface.

Lizzy finished piloting the ship for the first circle, and reported, "The circumference is 10,920 kilometers. So, the moon is about four times smaller than the Earth."

On our second circle, VC pointed and called out, "I see the NASA landing site."

The whole crew rushed over to look. The *Moon Lander* glinted in the rising sun.

We hovered over the landing site and were almost ready to go down to the surface.

As the mission leader I am also the safety officer. So, before we teleport to the surface, I have to make sure it is safe.

I was concerned about the temperature at the surface near the proposed landing site. I had been checking the surface temperature while we circled. It was hotter than boiling water in the direct sun and minus 130 degrees Celsius in the full dark. "It looks like the 1971 landing site temperature is OK," I announced. "Fortunately, it is in the area of sunrise."

I had Neddy, who was our *Scientist*, check the composition of the atmosphere. "Grandpa is correct about the moon restaurant," she reported. "There is no atmosphere. There are some molecules of oxygen, nitrogen, and other gases, but they are a billion, billion times fewer than they are on Earth. We won't be able to breathe. So, we'll have to use our helmets."

"OK gang," I said, "start planning how you are going to do your measurements. Neddy already did the composition of the atmosphere, and I did the surface temperature. We have the moon's circumference also. Now we just need to measure the weight of the moon, its density, its acceleration due to gravity, and the composition of the surface."

"Let's go," said Johari. "This is going to be the new GOAT." We all teleported to the surface.

"OK, everyone," I announced in my leader voice, "get going with the measurements of the moon's properties."

"Hey guys," Lizzy interrupted excitedly, "I can already tell that the moon's force of gravity is way less than on Earth. Look how high I can jump. The moon is much smaller than Earth, so it's pull on me is much smaller. VC and I will measure the acceleration due to gravity with my *Velocity* tool. VC can drop a rock, and I will measure the velocity change as it falls. VC will use a stopwatch so we know the time it takes for the fall. That will give us the acceleration due to gravity on the moon."

"I bet I can get the result faster," I challenged.

"You're on," Lizzy accepted. She and VC started making their measurements.

"Hey, Milo," I asked, "how much do I weigh?" Milo was the *Guardian* and had the *Mass and Weight* tool.

"Ten kilograms. That's twenty-two pounds," he answered.

I did a quick calculation in my head and announced, "The acceleration due to gravity is 1.6 meters per second per second. I win."

Ten minutes later, Lizzy and VC completed their velocity measurements. "OK, *Boy Genius*," said Lizzy, "how did you get the answer so fast? We got about the same value."

"Milo measured my weight on the moon as ten kilograms," I explained. "On Earth, I weigh sixty kilograms. So the force of gravity on the moon is one-sixth of that on Earth." VC looked impressed, so I kept going. "If the force of gravity is one-sixth, then the acceleration due to gravity is one-sixth also. So, one-sixth of the 9.8 meters per second per second acceleration on Earth is 1.6 meters per second per second on the moon."

"OK," said Lizzy patting my shoulder, "*Boy Genius* gets to keep his title."

"Hey, kids," Grandpa said, "how about visiting Astronaut Scott?"

We all started walking in the direction of the *Moon Lander* that we could see in the distance.

We arrived on the scene to see Colonel David Scott saluting the flag. Grandpa put his hand over his heart too. Us kids were a little more hyper, but Colonel Scott didn't seem to mind. He paid no attention to us, even when Milo and Lizzy took advantage of the low gravity to jump over his head.

Neddy, as the *Scientist*, was busy measuring the composition of the moon's surface. "It has a lot of the same elements as on Earth, but not exactly," she reported.

"It makes good sense that the Earth and moon should be similar," added Grandpa, who had finished saluting the flag and was back to helping us. "The theory of the moon's origin is that it formed from the debris kicked up when a huge asteroid hit Earth. So its composition should be a combination of Earth and the asteroid."

"OK," I said. "Two more things we have to determine are the mass of the moon and its density." We made the measurements and put them in a report at the end of the *Journal*.

"Let's see if our measurements are consistent," I said. "Let's compute the mass of the moon by using the formula: *Mass equals Density times Volume*. We can compute the moon's volume from the circumference that we measured."

We got the same seventy-three billion trillion kilograms. We put the complete moon mass calculation at the end of the *Journal*.

We had one more job to do. We had to measure the period for one full revolution around the Earth. We left the *Cosmic Egg* in place as our marker and advanced the time. It took 27.3 days for the moon to circle the Earth and arrive back at the starting point below us.

We had finished our assignments. We would now have to put our findings together in a report for the contest judges.

Before ending the mission, we spent the next hour exploring the moon and jumping over craters. Lizzy was able to do the biggest jump. So she is the crater-jumping champion as well as the gin rummy champ.

"I have a question," Richie said. "There are all of these craters covering the moon's surface. Why don't we see the same thing on Earth?"

"That's a good question," replied Grandpa. "There are a bunch of reasons. Smaller meteors burn up in Earth's atmosphere and never reach the surface. Some asteroids hit the water, like the one that killed the dinosaurs. You don't see any of the craters that slam into ocean floors. Some craters are destroyed by erosion or hidden by plant life. But there are lots of craters if you look for them. One of the best is the Barringer Meteorite Crater in Arizona. It is over a kilometer wide."

Grandpa asked if there were any other questions, but nobody had any.

"OK," I said, "great job, everyone. Our next mission is the Survey of the Solar System to find peculiar things. That should be interesting too."

9

PECULIAR THINGS IN THE SOLAR SYSTEM

(AS TOLD BY JOHARI)

I felt so glad to be in the *Race to the Big Bang Contest*. It was my best activity of the pandemic. Even better than Grandma's cooking classes that I was allowed to sit in on, even though she wasn't *my* grandma. The contest was definitely the GOAT. I loved our *Room* meetings, and the moon visit was lit. And it kept my brother from driving me completely crazy.

The contest and all the new pandemic routines were bringing back some amount of normalcy to my life in California. I started taking singing lessons. My mom signed me up with a voice coach who teaches online. Lizzy, VC, Neddy, and I were doing *Room* calls twice a week to talk about girl stuff. Lizzy saw my brother online when they played gin rummy, at which she is still winning. Neddy was FaceTiming with Richie, and of course Milo and Svetlana were a thing. But VC just has six-year-old Griffin for boy company. Like me, VC and I just have our brothers. Ugh!

I told the girls about this great new boy band that was playing free concerts on the Santa Monica pier. People were coming to listen and dance. A boy asked me to boogie with him. Everyone wore masks, so I wasn't sure I would ever recognize him again. The band leader saw me singing along to one of their songs and invited me up on stage. He handed me the microphone, and I sang three songs. It was way lit.

The last girl meeting was all about new clothes. I showed the girls my great collection of California boy-band T-shirts. They loved them.

In addition to those activities, I was taking a lot of pictures for Grandpa's wildlife photo contest. It was nothing but cute cats and dogs— not exactly wildlife. But finally, I got a pretty sure winner. On my morning run, I was going out to the end of the pier. Halfway there, I was stopped in my tracks by a crazy scene. There on a bench, sleeping like it was a

homeless person, was a sea lion. This was my best shot. Wow, I would have thought that the beach would have been a better place for a nap, but I'm not a sea lion.

I have been looking but no whale sightings yet. But I'm feeling confident with that sea lion shot.

At 11:00 a.m. Pacific time, we started our second *Qualifier* exercise, the Peculiar Things in the Solar System. I was nominated as the leader of this mission. I decided to keep Jackson as the *Safety Officer*.

When everyone was logged on, I went over the mission objectives. "OK, guys, this is what we have to do. One, we need to visit all eight planets plus Pluto. Two, we need to do the complete survey of the planet's physical properties like we did for the moon. **Three**, we need to find something peculiar and unique about each planet. And four, we need to submit a report on what we found. We have to produce a good report to qualify for the *Regionals*. There is a great NASA website called <u>Solar System Exploration</u> that we can use to get information. This mission could be the GOAT."

"Johari," interrupted Richie, "that's the second time you called something the goat. What's the goat?"

"Oh, sorry Richie," I answered. "It's a California thing. GOAT means <u>G</u>reatest <u>O</u>f <u>A</u>ll <u>T</u>ime."

"I have a suggestion," offered VC. "Let's make a table of properties with the first column naming the planets and the top row with all the things we need to measure, like the weight, atmosphere, temperature, composition, size, time for a complete orbit, and stuff like that."

"VC," I said, "we are spending way too much time together. We are starting to think alike. I already made the table. I filled in the numbers that we measured on the moon and those for Earth. I also put in the planet's distance from the sun." I brought it up on the computer screen.

"That was just what I had in mind," said VC. "Let's start with Mercury, the closest planet to the sun, and work our way out."

"Mercury it is. Let's go," I commanded.

VC, who was the *Navigator* for this trip, mimicked Lizzy with an "aye, aye, sir," and away from Earth we went. It would take us two minutes plus speed-up and slow-down to reach Mercury.

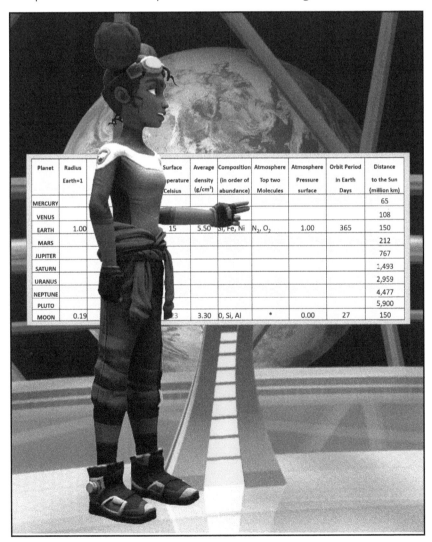

Planet	Radius Earth=1	Surface Temperature Celsius	Average density (g/cm³)	Composition (in order of abundance)	Atmosphere Top two Molecules	Atmosphere Pressure surface	Orbit Period in Earth Days	Distance to the Sun (million km)
MERCURY								65
VENUS								108
EARTH	1.00	15	5.50	Si, Fe, Ni	N₂, O₂	1.00	365	150
MARS								212
JUPITER								767
SATURN								1,493
URANUS								2,959
NEPTUNE								4,477
PLUTO								5,900
MOON	0.19		3.30	O, Si, Al	*	0.00	27	150

To kill time, Jackson and Lizzy continued their gin rummy tournament. VC and Neddy got into a discussion with Milo about high school. They wanted to know all about the experience.

I started singing a song my dad loves: *"Fly me to the moon. Let me play among the stars. Let me see what a spring is like on Jupiter and Mars."* I got weird looks from the team, so I stopped.

Richie started telling bad jokes. This was becoming his thing. It was almost as bad as having VC's six-year-old brother around. "What do planets like to read?" he asked and then answered, "Comet books. How do space aliens serve dinner? On flying saucers."

Most of the team groaned. Neddy glared at him and said, "Zip it, Richie. I'd rather hear Johari singing."

When we got to Mercury, Jackson did his job as our *Safety Officer*.

"Problemo," Jackson said when we arrived. "We are not going down to the surface. The surface temperature is pizza-oven hot, like over four hundred degrees Celsius. We have to do all the measurements from the *Cosmic Egg*."

Neddy launched her drone to get a picture of Mercury with the *Cosmic Egg* in front.

"OK, team," I said, "let's get to work on the measurements."

"Jack," Lizzy asked, "is measuring your weight aboard the ship still good for determining Mercury's gravity?"

"It'll be OK," said Jack. "The measurement will be a little smaller because we are stationed one hundred kilometers above the surface, but I'll correct for that."

"I tested out the new *Distance* tool," said Milo. "I just have to point it at a distant object, and it reads the distance to it. We are sixty-five million kilometers from the sun."

"Now, guys," I asked when we finished our measurements, "what is peculiar about Mercury?"

"I think it is the size of the sun when you look at it from here," offered Richie. "It looks three times bigger than on Earth."

"I see something peculiar too," said Neddy. "Mercury hasn't rotated at all since we have been here. The side that was in daylight when we got here is still in daylight."

"I'll move us back in time to see how long it takes to turn," VC said as she programmed a time hop. "Wow, it has taken almost fifty-nine days for the sunrise area of Mercury to become sunset and go back to sunrise again. That is 1,408 hours. Talk about long, boring days."

We voted that the 1,408-hour Mercury day was its most peculiar thing.

◢ ◢ ◢ ◢ ◢

After a short break, we traveled on to Venus.

"Why is Venus named after the Roman goddess of beauty?" asked Richie. "Because it's the hottest planet in our solar system."

"That one isn't too bad," I said, chuckling.

"We have to work from the *Cosmic Egg* again," announced Jack. "The Venus surface temperature is even hotter than on Mercury. We'd be cooked in an instant in its almost seven-hundred-degree Celsius atmosphere."

We did all the physical measurements. "Venus has an atmosphere of mostly carbon dioxide," Neddy reported.

"That's why Venus is hotter than Mercury, even though it is farther from the sun," explained Jackson. "It is similar to the global

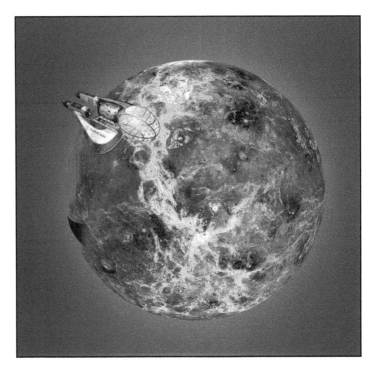

warming problem on Earth. The carbon dioxide absorbs the radiation coming from the surface and sends half of it back. That returned energy heats up the planet instead of going off into space to cool it. And that makes the surface hotter."

We measured the length of the Venus day, and it was even longer than a Mercury day.

"It is almost six thousand hours long," reported VC. "That's two-thirds of a year."

"OK," I said, "is that its peculiar thing?"

"Hey, guys," Neddy offered, "I measured small amounts of phosphine gas in the Venus atmosphere. I thought that might be peculiar, so I did a Google search. In a recent paper, scientists asserted that there could be something currently alive on Venus. That is the most likely explanation for phosphine's source. But how could life survive in the hot atmosphere of Venus?"

After much discussion, the *Cosmic Explorers* team agreed that possible life on Venus is its most peculiar thing.

Having finished the two planets that are closer to the sun than Earth, we decided to wait until the following day to do those that are farther from the sun. Mars would be our next stop. Grandpa was coming too.

■ ■ ■ ■ ■

"Good news, everyone," announced Jackson. "We can go down to the Martian surface. Dress warm. The temperature in the sun today is ten degrees Celsius. And wear your breathing helmets; there is very little atmosphere, and it's mostly carbon dioxide."

While we were circling the planet, we saw something reflecting the sun. On close inspection, we determined it was the Mars Rover Curiosity sent by NASA in 2011. Grandpa remembered some of the people who worked on the team.

"Let's go there," Richie said, smiling.

"I'd like to see it." We teleported to the surface.

"This is one cool piece of equipment," Jack said, walking up and checking it out. We took lots of pictures, including one of Grandpa that he sent to some of his old NASA coworkers.

We measured all of Mars' physical parameters, and nothing was really unusual.

"I think the Mars Rover is the planet's most peculiar thing," said Lizzy. "It's the only other planet besides Earth that has had a vehicle driving around on its surface."

With that decided, we teleported back to the Cosmic Egg and headed for Jupiter.

"Well," said Jack, "the temperature of the atmosphere is really cold, about minus 145 Celsius. But maybe the surface is OK."

"I'll go down and check it out," I offered. So, I dressed in the warmest spacesuit I could find and teleported to the surface. I hit the atmosphere, and it was cold. My avatar started to turn blue, but I kept going lower, and it got warmer. But no matter how far I went down, there was no surface. Finally, I reported back to the crew. "We can't go down to the surface of Jupiter. There doesn't appear to be a surface. Almost the whole planet is made of gas, mainly hydrogen."

I teleported back to the ship, and we got to work doing our measurements from there.

Lizzy called out, "It has more than three hundred times the mass of Planet Earth."

Neddy reported, "The clouds that make up the bands are made of ammonia crystals and sulfur."

We did a circle around the planet, and VC announced, "Jupiter is over eleven times bigger than Earth. For the most peculiar thing, I vote for the big red spot on the surface."

"It is definitely peculiar," I added. "According to *Solar System Exploration*, the Great Red Spot is a huge storm on Jupiter. It has raged for at least 350 years, and it is so large that three Earths could fit inside it."

The Great Red Spot got the vote for Jupiter's most peculiar thing.

Like Jupiter, Saturn was also a giant gas planet.

Milo said immediately, "The most peculiar thing about Saturn is the rings."

"The rings are made of chunks of ice and rock," announced Neddy who was busy using her *Composition* tool. "And the planet itself is mostly hydrogen and helium gas."

"Here is another candidate for most peculiar," said VC. "Saturn has eighty-two moons."

"Wasn't there a space probe that went to Saturn?" asked Richie.

"Yes," answered Grandpa.

"But it was vaporized in Saturn's atmosphere in 2017," added Jackson, the showoff.

Saturn's rings and the eighty-two moons got the team's vote for most peculiar things. Hopefully, both were right. We took a break before going on.

As we approached Uranus, Grandpa requested that we all line up for a group photo with the planet in the background out the front windows. We even let the clone pets out of the equipment room for the photo. Grandpa took the picture.

Getting the pets back into the equipment room was a huge pain.

"Uranus is known as the Ice Giant," said Neddy. "Its composition is water, methane, and ammonia."

"It is also known as the Sideways Planet," said VC, "because it rotates on its side. All the other planets turn on an axis that gives both halves a night and a day. But Uranus rotates so that half the planet is always pointed at the sun to make one half permanent day and another half permanent night."

"I know something peculiar about Uranus," offered Grandpa. "There was an article about it in the *Washington Post* a couple of years ago. Astronomers think that the atmosphere of Uranus rains diamonds. They believe that under the high-pressure and carbon-rich environment, diamonds will form. How about that for peculiar?"

The team voted that the Sideways Planet with diamond rain were the most peculiar features of Uranus.

⧹⧹⧹⧹⧹

We traveled on to Neptune, which was 4.5 billion kilometers from the sun.

Richie, of course, had another joke. "What kind of music do planets like? Neptunes," he answered.

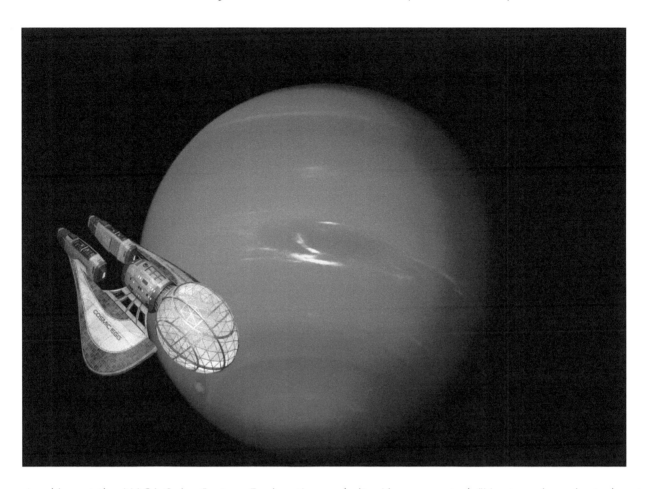

Looking at the NASA Solar System Exploration website, Lizzy reported, "Neptune is a giant planet, four times larger than Earth. Its atmosphere is made of hydrogen, helium, and methane. Methane gives the planet its blue color."

We measured all Neptune's properties and got its most peculiar thing from the NASA website: "Neptune is our solar system's windiest world. Clouds of frozen methane whip across the planet at speeds of more than 2,000 km/h (1,200 mph). That's close to the top speed of a fighter jet. Earth's most powerful winds hit only about 400 km/h (250 mph)."

▰ ▰ ▰ ▰ ▰

Our final destination was Pluto. At our top speed of one million kilometers per second, the trip would take over one and a half hours. We used the time to put together what we had already discovered into a report for the contest.

"You know," said Grandpa, pointing at us all, "when I was your age, Pluto was the ninth planet. But it is small, about the same size as our moon, and it has only one-fifth the moon's mass. So, astronomers demoted it to a dwarf planet, and now we only have eight full planets in the solar system."

"I think that should be its peculiar thing," said Lizzy. "It's the only planet that ever got demoted."

Everyone, even Richie the joker, laughed. When we got to Pluto, Jack did his *Safety Officer* thing. "Not going down to the surface," he said. "Way too cold. It's minus 233 Celsius."

"Hey," said Richie, "it kinda looks like the moon with all the craters."

We made all the measurements and went with Pluto's demotion as its peculiar thing.

To end our mission, we entered all of the physical parameters for each planet into my Table of Planet Properties, and we made a table of each planet's most peculiar things. We submitted them, together with our pictures, for our report.

PLANET	MOST PECULIAR THING
MERCURY	1,408-hour day
VENUS	Possible signs of life
EARTH	Human life
MARS	Earth vehicle driving around on its surface
JUPITER	The 350-year-old Great Red Spot storm
SATURN	Saturn's rings and eighty-two moons
URANUS	The Sideways Planet that rains diamonds
NEPTUNE	The windiest planet
PLUTO	The only planet to get demoted to dwarf planet

VC and I also composed a rap about our mission:

PLANET RAP

To visit all the planets is a mission that's long.
A billion-mile trip like that is worth a song.
Some planets are solid, and some are gas.
And except for Pluto, they have lots of mass.
Some are way hot, and some are way cold,
all are more than four billion years old.
Pluto, Uranus, Jupiter, and Mars,
Our neighboring planets that look like stars.

Some planets are big, and some are small,
The star that's our sun shines on them all.
Afternoons on Mercury have lots of time for play,
On a hot rock with a fourteen-hundred-hour day.
For the longest day, Venus is the winner.
One-third of a year between breakfast and dinner.
If vacations on Pluto are yearlong stays,
Pack plenty of provisions for ninety-thousand days.
Mercury, Venus, Pluto, and Mars
Are some more planets that look like stars.

Astronomers see some signs of life on Venus.
It's hard to check with millions of miles between us.
Some planets have atmosphere, and some have none.
If you need to breathe oxygen, Earth's the only one.
Saturn is special because of rings around it.
I searched with my telescope; I'm glad I found it.
Blue Neptune is the windiest planet yet.
Winds blowing at speeds of a supersonic jet.
Venus, Saturn, Neptune, and Mars,
Our neighboring planets that look like stars.

10

PECULIAR THINGS IN THE OCEAN

[AS TOLD BY MILO]

Svetlana and I were continuing to take our socially distanced walks. She was still fun to talk to even though her team was doing the *Qualifying* missions too. She told me that they got a really famous Russian physicist to join their team. He was a friend of her father when they lived in Russia. I wished her good luck in the race, but since our teams were competing, we agreed not to talk about it anymore.

I was the leader for our *Peculiar Things in the Ocean* mission, which I annoyingly had to leave Svetlana to go do. The kids, without the adults, were going to take the *Cosmic Egg* on an ocean dive to see interesting things in the undersea world. The first part of the mission was to find peculiar sea creatures to photograph. The more difficult part was to find the wreck of the luxury cruise ship Titanic. It hit an iceberg and sank to the bottom of the ocean in 1912. We had to locate it somewhere in the vast North Atlantic Ocean. We knew only that it sank six hundred kilometers south-southeast of Newfoundland. We had to submit a report on it, which would be judged.

We all logged on to the *Virtual World* and teleported from the *Mystery Museum* to the *Cosmic Egg*. We headed for the crystal-clear waters of the Caribbean for our first dive.

Scene from "The Stardust Mystery Online - Introduction." The STARDUST MYSTERY YouTube Channel

"Wow," Neddy shouted as we got to the shallow bottom. The scene outside the *Cosmic Egg* was amazing. It was beautiful. "Can we use our dive equipment and go outside the ship?"

"Sure," I said. "Awesome idea."

We put on our equipment, and out we went. It was a fantastic world of coral and beautiful sea creatures. The sunlight sparkled and rippled on the bottom as it was bent by the waves above.

"Look at all the turtles," Neddy called out. "I love turtles."

There were beautifully colored fish, jellyfish, and sharks too. We explored for over two hours. Then we headed for different parts of the ocean to find some unusual fish. We saw and took pictures of a *Siamese Battle Fish* and a giant *Whale Shark*.

"This is cool," yelled Lizzy pointing out the front window. "It's a fish with a big head and lots of sharp teeth." Johari and VC went over to take a closer look.

The three of them were staring at what we found out later was a *piranha*. I went to the *Cosmic Egg* controls and did a quick reduction of our size by a factor of fifty. All of a sudden, the sharp teeth were looming outside the front window. The girls screamed and scattered.

I went quickly back to normal size so that thing wouldn't swallow us. That could get us disqualified before even getting through the *Qualifying* round.

When the girls had figured out what had happened and who had done it, they surrounded me.

"You are going to so pay for that," threatened Lizzy.

"Just you wait," growled Johari.

"We are going to get sweet revenge," agreed VC.

"I think it was a genius move," Jackson said for boy solidarity, even though I got him too.

"Let's see if we can find some other unusual sea life," I said.

Richie called and pointed out a side window. "Hey, guys, look at that fish. It looks really strange."

"I know what that is," said Neddy. "It is an anglerfish. There was one in *Finding Nemo*. An angler is a fisherman, and this fish has a bioluminescent 'fishing pole' that hangs bait for its prey just in front of its huge mouth."

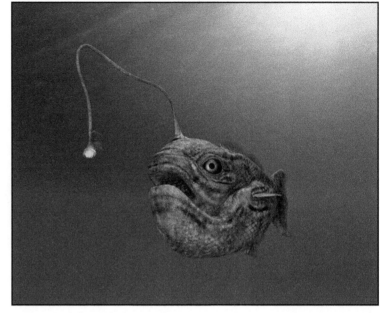

While we were searching with our eyes for new fish, Neddy was using her *Composition* tool to look for chemical elements indicative of life. We followed an interesting trail of carbon and nitrogen readings and came to an area where there was liquid gushing out of the sea floor.

I did a measurement with my *Temperature* tool and found the liquid to be over one hundred degrees Celsius. We did a computer search and found that these fountains of hot liquid were called hydrothermal vents.

"It looks like there is a lot of carbon where the hydrothermal vent fluids mix with the surrounding seawater," announced Neddy.

We sucked up some of the carbon-rich fluid and examined it under our microscope. It looked like a bunch of fish eggs; tiny little spheres clumped together. We did a search on life in hydrothermal vents and found out that what we were seeing were hyperthermophiles. These are microorganisms that can live at temperatures of ninety degrees Celsius and above.

"The temperature there is one hundred and ten degrees Celsius," I said. "An organism that can live at that temperature is awesome!"

"Maybe that's the kind of life that can live in the hot atmosphere of Venus that we saw evidence of on our solar system tour," offered Johari.

"OK team," I said, "let's finish this mission. We have to find the wreck of the Titanic." I was the *Navigator* for the mission, so I entered our destination as six hundred kilometers south-southeast of Newfoundland. I also really wanted to finish up to go see if I could take Svetlana on an underwater adventure date on *Mission KT*.

We came out of the ocean and flew above the water. When we got to the location, we all looked around.

VC said, "There's a lot of ocean out there. How do we find the shipwreck?"

Jackson came up with a brilliant idea. "Hey guys, since the *Cosmic Egg* time travels, let's go back in time to just before the Titanic sank and follow it."

"It sank just after April 14, 1912," added Johari.

We traveled back to the day of the sinking. There were plenty of icebergs in the water, but we did not see the Titanic.

"I'll search for iron with my *Composition* tool," offered Neddy. She did a 360-degree sweep of the area. "I got a faint iron signal off to the right."

We followed the signal as it got stronger. "I see smoke," said Lizzy. We followed the smoke and finally saw the Titanic steaming full speed ahead. We followed it until it hit the iceberg.

"I already saw the Titanic sink in the movie," Lizzy begged. "I really don't want to see that again."

I supported her because I was in a secret hurry. "OK," I said, "let's head back to the present time now that we have the exact location."

When we were back in the present, we dove the *Cosmic Egg* to the ocean bottom, but there was no sign of the shipwreck.

"I'll use my *Composition* tool again to look for iron," said Neddy.

We followed the signal, and about two miles from the starting location, we spotted it. It was looming out of the ocean's darkness, crusted with sea life.

"It's kinda creepy," whispered VC. "It's so big and silent. It is clearly a picture of something that went very, very wrong."

"I agree," said Neddy. "I can almost see the ghosts of the passengers who went down with the ship."

We circled around the wreck and took some pictures to complete our mission.

"Let's go home," Neddy said. "I'm feeling kinda sad."

That's what we did. I wrote up the mission for our *Journal* and to submit for the *Qualifying Round*. Then I went to see about my date.

11

PROVING
THE BIG BANG THEORY

(AS TOLD BY LIZZY)

I was no longer depressed. I loved getting up in the morning again. Dad was out of the basement and feeling cheerful. Neddy and I were back to our old routines, bugging each other and making up. But now it was something I was glad to have. Our *Room* meetings with the *Cosmic Explorer* team had been interesting, and our visits in the *Virtual World* had been so way cool. Life was nearly normal.

For our last *Qualifying Mission*, I was in charge. Our task was to pick up Professor Georges Lemaître, who created the theory of the *Big Bang*. He had called it the *Hypothesis of the Cosmic Egg*. We loved the name, so we called our travel ship the *Cosmic Egg*. Scientists later dubbed his theory the *Big Bang*. We'll use our *Cosmic Egg* to time travel and measure the distance to the Andromeda Galaxy as we go back in time. That will get us data to prove Lemaître's theory of a universe expanding from a single point.

For the mission, we used headsets for voice communication. "OK," I instructed, "everyone has to log in to the *Virtual World*."

"I'm ready," said VC, followed by Neddy, Richie, Jackson, and Johari.

"Hey," I said, "Milo, are you here?" There was no response. Milo wasn't with us.

"Has anyone heard from Milo?" I asked. No one had talked to him. I tried texting him. No answer. It was really strange. It was the *Mystery of the Missing Milo*. "OK, we will have to do this mission without him. We'll make him do a bunch of extra work to make up for this."

We all logged on, went to the *Mystery Museum*, and teleported to the *Cosmic Egg*.

"Johari, you're the *Navigator* for this trip. Program us for Leuven, Belgium, in 1927."

"Aye, aye, sir," Johari said in our now-routine response to the mission commander.

We were moving away from the *Mystery Museum*. There were weird sounds, and the building below us disappeared.

"Awesome!" I said as we warped back in time. "Look outside. It looks like we are going through a tunnel." At the end of the tunnel, there was a beautiful old city below us.

Neddy launched her drone that had a video camera. We were looking for the Catholic University of Leuven. "I'll put the picture up on the large monitor," she said. Finally, the drone flew over what we were pretty sure was the university.

"Oh, wow, that is so weird," said Neddy. "There is a T-Rex on the campus. How could that be happening? There shouldn't be a T-Rex running around Belgium in 1927."

"And look at that," VC screamed as she ran over to the screen. "There is a guy dressed like a priest running away from the T-Rex, and some papers he was carrying are going flying into the sky."

"Professor Lemaître is a Catholic priest," observed Johari. "I'll bet that's him."

"Yeah," I agreed, "the guy running has got to be Georges Lemaître. We'd better save him."

So, we flew the *Cosmic Egg* to a spot over the university, and we all teleported to the surface.

"I got this," said Jackson. "I'll use my best *Guardian* tool."

He set his tool selection wheel to *Time-Freeze*, pointed at the T-Rex, and zapped it. The T-Rex instantly stopped moving and stood still like it had been fast-frozen.

VC yelled, "Good job, Jack. Keep that monster frozen while I take some pictures. We can use them for our report."

"While you two do that," I said, taking back control, "Neddy and I will go talk to Professor Lemaître to find out what happened. Hey, Neddy, let's pick up the papers that he dropped."

"Wait," said Jackson, "I'll go with you." He gave the T-Rex another jolt of *Time-Freeze* and ran after us.

"Hi, Professor Lemaître," I greeted. "We are the *Cosmic Explorer* crew, and we are on a *Race to the Big Bang*. We saw that you were in trouble and came to help. Can you tell us what happened?"

"*Je ne comprends pas*," answered Lemaître. "*Parlez-vous Francais?*"

Then I remembered that Professor Lemaître spoke French, so I called, "Hey, VC, stop taking pictures and come translate for us."

VC ran over to us and started talking to Professor Lemaître. After a while, she turned to us and told us what they had talked about. "The professor said that earlier today, he had another visit from another group of kids. He said there were two girls who looked exactly the same, plus another girl and two boys."

"That must have been Svetlana's team, the *Brooklyn Bunch*," I suggested.

"Sounds right," answered Neddy. "But there should only be four of them. Who was the *extra* boy?"

I didn't say anything, but I had a bad feeling.

VC continued the story. "Professor Lemaître said that they apologized for being late, but they had made a mistake setting their time clock. When they first warped to that time and place, they saw dinosaurs."

"I would never make a mistake like that as *Navigator*," Johari assured us.

"According to Professor Lemaître," VC continued, "they looked at their time clock, saw it was sixty-five million years ago, and realized their mistake. They came here and found him, but they couldn't understand each other because they only spoke English and Russian, and he only spoke French. While they were trying to talk, a dinosaur appeared and started to chase them. The kids zoomed up to their ship and took off, leaving Professor Lemaître as bait for the beast. That's when we arrived. He thanked us for saving him."

"Tell him we are time traveling," I suggested. "Ask him whether he will go with us for a while, and tell him these are the papers he dropped." I handed him the papers.

VC talked to the professor and then translated for us. "He thanks us for saving his papers. They were the calculations for his theory. He said that he would be happy to go with us if we help him prove his hypothesis of the *Cosmic Egg*. He asked whether we could make measurements to show that the universe was smaller at earlier times."

"Oh, yeah," I responded, "we already planned to do that. Tell him we will measure the distance from Earth to the nearest galaxy, *Andromeda,* at each point in time. If the whole universe was smaller at earlier times, that distance will be smaller too."

VC repeated what I said to the professor and then told us, "He said 'wonderful. That would be perfect.'"

"I'm gonna make a clone of the T-Rex," said Neddy who was our *Scientist*. She launched her drone and flew it through the blue rings above the T-Rex. A little copy of the dinosaur appeared on the ground. "I am going to take him with us. He will be my pet, and I am naming him T. He'll be able to keep Rexy company, so she doesn't make such a racket when she is left in the equipment room."

That made no sense to me since there were now already like a bajillion pet dinosaurs in the equipment room. But with Neddy, a girl had to pick her battles.

"Before we head back to the *Cosmic Egg,* why don't we look for some gems to start our *Currency Account*?" suggested Johari. "There is a museum on campus, and maybe we can find some good things to clone."

"While you guys are doing that," I said, "Neddy and I are going to look around. Our mom said our great-grandmother used to work at this university. I want to see if we can find her."

Johari, Jackson, Richie, and VC headed to the museum. Neddy and I started to walk around the campus with T tagging along. The little T-Rex clone bumped into me. I turned to face it and complained loudly, "Neddy, keep your stupid pet out of my way."

The baby T-Rex responded by jumping and nipping at me. I took on a martial arts threatening pose, and the T-Rex ran behind Neddy for protection. "Don't be afraid of her, T," said Neddy. "I'll protect you."

Neddy and I continued roaming, looking for young women who might be the right age. There was a woman in a booth at the school's entrance.

"Neddy," I whispered, "she kinda looks like you."

"Hi," I said to the woman. My name is Lizzy, and this is my sister, Neddy. Do you speak English?"

"A little," she responded. "My name is Mary. You girls look familiar. Do I know you?"

She had my great-grandmother's first name, but when I asked what her last name was, it wasn't right.

"Do you have any children?" I asked.

"No," she responded, "I'm not married."

I was now almost certain she was my great-grandmother. She looked so much like Neddy and had the right first name.

"Mary," I said, "I am pretty sure that in the near future, you are going to get married. You are going to have three children. You're going to name your second child Peter, and he will become a scientist."

"Oh," Neddy said to me, "Peter is Grandpa."

Mary looked at me with a big frown, like maybe I was a bit crazy. But then she smiled. She came out of her booth and gave me and Neddy hugs. Then we said goodbye.

▰▰▰▰▰

When the other kids were leaving the museum, Neddy and I were coming across the courtyard.

"So?" called Johari. "Did you find a long-lost relative?"

"I think so," I replied. "We found a woman of the right age with the right first name, and she looked like Neddy's twin. I am pretty sure she is our great-grandmother."

"Wow, that is so cool," said VC.

Jackson told us about their museum visit. "Inside there was an exhibit on diamonds mined in the Belgium Congo. It featured the largest diamond ever mined. Richie made a clone of it using the *Scientist's* tool that Neddy had loaned him. We shipped it back to the Cosmic Egg."

"We saw something else that we thought might be valuable," said Johari. "The sign said they were geodes, a round rock that contains a hollow cavity lined with crystals. One had been cut in half. Richie made a clone of that too."

"Well team," I suggested, "it is time to leave. Let's get Professor Lemaître and teleport to the ship."

Professor Lemaître asked VC what to do. She told him that he just had to step into the yellow beam, and he would automatically teleport to the ship. He teleported up, and we all followed. We also took the time-frozen T-Rex. We planned to take it back to sixty-five million years ago to fix the timeline error that Svetlana's team may have created.

When we were all onboard, Professor Lemaître asked about measuring the distance to *Andromeda*. So, Johari used our telescope function to find *Andromeda* and then planted a beacon. Her computer then showed that the distance to the beacon was 2.5 million light years at the current time, the year 1927.

Johari, who was typing furiously on her computer, said, "Wow, guys, that's like twenty-five billion, billion kilometers. That is such a long distance away. If we went there in a real spaceship, we would never live long enough to arrive."

VC took a picture of the *Andromeda* distance measurement and added it to some of the other pictures from Belgium for our report.

"OK everyone," I announced, "the final thing we need to do is to go back to sixty-five million years ago and fix the timeline error that Svetlana's team probably created."

It took us sixty-five seconds to travel back the sixty-five million years. Jackson, Johari, and I teleported to the surface with the frozen T-Rex. We took pictures as it unfroze back in its own time.

Then I asked, "Hey guys, what caused the timeline error, and how do we fix it?"

Jackson said, "If the T-Rex was present in 1927, maybe the <u>asteroid that killed the dinosaurs</u> didn't hit Earth, and so they weren't all wiped out. Maybe Svetlana's team flew too close to the asteroid or did something else that pulled it off course."

"I'll move us forward in time," said Johari. "If the asteroid misses Earth, my brother is right."

Sure enough, the asteroid didn't hit Earth. It just whizzed right past. It made a flaming path in the atmosphere and gigantic ocean waves, but no impact. *Boy Genius* had done it again.

"OK," said Jackson, "now all we have to do is get the asteroid back on course."

So, we went back to the time the asteroid was approaching Earth. Jackson had Johari measure its position and velocity. Then he did some calculations. "That should do it," he said as he applied his *time-freeze* tool three times to the asteroid. "Let's go forward in time and make sure."

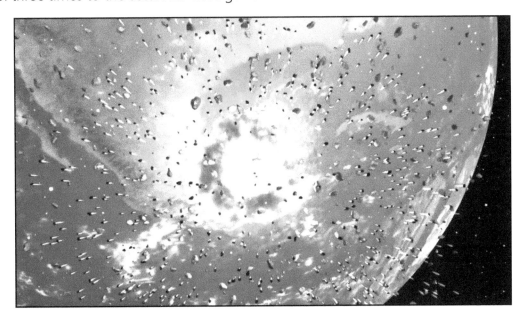

Scene from "What Killed the Land Dinosaurs?" The STARDUST MYSTERY YouTube Channel

We traveled a short while forward in time. Sure enough, the asteroid hit the Earth right off the coast of Mexico, just as it was supposed to.

Finally, we measured the distance to *Andromeda* at sixty-five million years ago and found that it was smaller by one-tenth percent. Professor Lemaître was delighted.

We returned Professor Lemaître to his own time, doing one more *Andromeda* distance measurement along the way. The distance change confirmed his *Big Bang* predictions. That completed our mission.

Unfortunately, we still had not heard from Milo, but I had a suspicion about *why*.

PART 3
THE REGIONALS
(LATE MAY AND JUNE)

RICHIE'S BRILLIANT IDEA

(AS TOLD BY RICHIE)

After we logged off, I found a text on my phone from Milo addressed to me and the rest of the team. It said, "Sorry, guys. I'm joining Svetlana's team. I already told G-pa. I know you will do well without me. I hope you can forgive me." It was signed "Milo" and had sad-face emojis.

"Well," I said to myself, "that solves the *Mystery of the Missing Milo*. I guess he was the extra boy with Svetlana's team. We'll just have to win this contest without him."

I had told the team that I had a unique idea for our space station, and I did. We were going to have a *Room* meeting for me to present it and for the team to discuss it. But before the meeting, I wanted to go over it with Neddy. I called her and then headed over to her house.

Neddy met me at the door wearing a mask and had me put mine on before I could come in. I wasn't in the family bubble. She took me up to her room to show me the pictures from the moon trip. They were cool. I was sorry I missed *that* contest, but better late to the team than never.

It was warm, so we went outside to sit on the back porch, where we could take our masks off.

"Hey, Dee, did you get the text from Milo?" I asked.

"Yeah, I did," she answered pretty icily. "If you ask me, I say it stinks. How come Svetlana stuck with *her* family, and Milo didn't? Not nice."

"I agree," I said. "He's a traitor."

"How are you and your family doing with the lockdown?" asked Neddy.

"Not great," I answered. "Nobody has gotten sick, but Mom, Dad, and my brother, Leo, are totally crabby. This was a good chance for me to get out of the house. The contest is the brightest part of my life now. I don't like the remote classes. I screwed up the online math test. I bet *you* did fine."

"Yeah," said Neddy, "I did fine. OK, let's do something positive. What is this great plan of yours?"

"This is my idea, Dee," I answered. "I looked up how they built the *International Space Station*. It took ten years and thirty missions into space to complete it. Even if we build something smaller, it is going to take lots of trips back seven billion years in time to bring all the parts. Remember, it took 65 seconds to go back in time sixty-five million years ago. That means each trip to seven billion years ago will take seven thousand seconds. That's over two hours. We could chew up lots of screen time doing that."

"You are right, Richie," agreed Neddy.

"So," I continued, "instead of bringing a bunch of parts to build the space station, my idea is to build the station from parts that we can find in space seven billion years ago. Then we only have to take one trip back in time."

"I think it's an interesting idea," offered Neddy. "But can we find all the parts we need?"

"First off," I said, "we find a planet that is the right distance from its star so that the temperature is comfortable for us. The planet itself would be our space station. It would be best if we can find one with an oxygen atmosphere and water like on Earth, but that probably won't happen. So, for water, we could find a comet, size change to tow it, and force it to crash into our planet. Then, boom, we have water."

"Wait a minute," interrupted Neddy. "There could be a flaw in your argument. If you are going to do a size change, why not just do a size change from the start so you can take all the parts and equipment with you on the first trip?"

"Oops, you're right," I agreed. "I guess it's not such a good idea after all."

"Don't give up so quickly," she argued. "Taking a big ship back in time may use more resources and take more time than the regular-size *Cosmic Egg*."

We jumped up, put on our masks, and went back inside to the computer. We logged on and did a quick check of the time for time travel versus the ship size. We found that increasing the ship size by a factor of two consumed twice the resources and took twice as long to time travel.

"So," I said, "I guess I'm back in business. We just need to figure out how to get a breathable atmosphere. Let's get the rest of the guys to help with that problem in the team meeting."

"It's a good thing that you didn't say anything about your idea before," observed Neddy. "Otherwise, Milo would have known about it, and he might have used it for Svetlana's team."

The doorbell rang, and I knew who it was. "I bet that is my little brother, Leo. He's having a problem, and he wanted to talk to you about it. He thinks you know everything."

"I kinda do," Neddy said smirking. "OK, I'll get him to come around to the back porch." She went to the front window, banged on it, and motioned for him to go around back.

Leo was sixteen months younger than me, but he was big and looked like me. A lot of people mistook us for twins.

"Hi, Leo," Neddy greeted when he came around the back. "Wassup?"

"Hi, Neddy," said Leo. "Did you know I started circus school? I love it, especially the trapeze. I'm the best in my class. I am also learning the tight rope. We do it with a really low rope so it isn't scary. I'm pretty good at that too."

"Cool," responded Neddy. "Richie said you were having a problem. What is it?"

"It's kinda embarrassing," Leo began. "This girl Robbin in my circus school says that I'm her boy-friend, and she wants me to kiss her. Ugh. How do I get her to stop?"

Neddy laughed and said, "That story reminds me of what Lizzy and VC did when Lizzy was nine. They decided that they needed to be prepared for kissing when the time came. So, one day, I caught them kissing their pillows like they were actual faces. At the time, I thought it was way gross and weird, but the whole scene was pretty funny. Tell her to try it on a pillow if she wants practice for when she really does have a boyfriend!"

"I can even give her a pillow as a present," suggested Leo.

"Good idea," Neddy agreed.

I rolled my eyes at the both of them.

Leo shoved off so that Neddy and I could plan how to present the space station idea to the team.

13

BRAINSTORMING

(AS TOLD BY NEDDY)

We called a general team meeting on *Room* for noon the day after Richie and I met. Everyone showed up by 12:05 EST, which stands for Eastern Standard Time. All the kids said hi to Grandpa, Tom, and Professor Nelson, who had told us to call her Helen.

"Did everyone see the email from TSI that came this morning?" I asked excitedly. "We passed the *Qualifying Round*!"

Everyone cheered.

"I should also mention, even though everyone knows, that we lost Milo to the *Brooklyn Bunch*."

Everyone booed until Grandpa shushed us. I guess he still *had* to love Milo since he was his grandson.

"It looks like the big prize money brought out a lot of competition," VC chimed in. "There are more than one hundred teams competing in our Northeast region and more than a thousand in the United States."

"And there are over four thousand when you add in the other countries," said Lizzy, who was reading the email on her phone. "That's a way lot of competition. It is not going to be that easy for us to win."

"So," said Johari, "let's focus on winning the *Regionals*. We have to build the best space station. Richie, do you want to tell us about your idea?"

"Yep," answered Richie. "Dee and I went over the idea yesterday. If we can solve one last problem, it could be a winning plan."

Richie had been calling me Dee for a few weeks now. At first, I wasn't sure, but now I liked it.

Richie and I took turns explaining the idea. We described how we could choose a planet that had the right temperature and how we could add water to the planet by capturing a few comets.

"This is why we think the idea is better than assembling parts like they did with the *International Space Station*," said Richie. "Building from parts will require lots of trips back in time to carry them, and that will use lots of resources and screen time."

"Or," I continued, "we can make the ship really big so we only have to make one trip. But Richie and I logged into the *Virtual World* and did a test to check that out. We found out that If we make the ship twice as big, it takes twice as long to time travel and uses twice the resources."

"Hold on," said Johari. "Why can't we make the ship really big, load all the parts, and then change size to really small to go back seven billion years? If your test was correct, being small would use almost no screen time or resources."

"Good thinking, sis," added Jackson. "But can you make the ship really small with all the parts onboard? We still have that geode onboard that we collected in Leuven. Let's check to see whether shrinking the ship also shrinks the geode."

Jackson and Johari logged on to the *Virtual World* to check it out. Five minutes later, Jackson reported, "We were able to shrink the ship's size until the geode filled the equipment room. Then it stopped shrinking. So, it looks like you wouldn't be able to shrink the ship filled with space station parts."

"Then Richie's idea is still good," said Lizzy. "So, what is the final problem we need to solve?"

"It's oxygen," Richie stated. "We need a breathable atmosphere, and I don't see how we can bring enough oxygen to fill the atmosphere of a planet."

"Green slime is the answer," Grandpa declared.

All the kids got puzzled looks on their faces. "You're joking, right, Grandpa?" I asked.

"No joke," answered Grandpa. "We do it the same way that Earth got its breathable atmosphere. The green slime, also known as cyanobacteria, produces oxygen by photosynthesis using sunlight and carbon dioxide."

"Grandpa is right," offered Tom. "Our atmosphere was mostly carbon dioxide when Earth first formed. But about three and a half billion years ago, the one-celled cyanobacteria microorganisms started converting the carbon dioxide into carbon for growth. The oxygen from the carbon dioxide was released."

Tom paused before continuing. "At first, the cyanobacteria were almost exclusively in the oceans, and the oxygen was released there. But about two billion years ago, oxygen started getting released into the atmosphere. That is called the Great Oxygen Event. The atmospheric concentration of oxygen continued to grow, hitting our current 21% of the atmosphere about five hundred million years ago."

"Here is a picture of the slimy stuff that is responsible for us being here on Earth," Grandpa said as he shared his screen with us.

"Whoa," exclaimed Richie. "You mean we have to thank that green crud for the air that we breathe?"

"Absolutely right," continued Grandpa. It is totally responsible for us being alive here on Earth."

"So," said Richie, catching on to the idea, "we could collect green slime from Earth and take it back to the planet we want as our space station, say, at eight billion years ago. Then, by seven billion years ago, we will have a planet with an oxygen atmosphere?"

"Yes," Tom and Grandpa said together.

"The question is," added Helen, "can we find the right planet to use for our space station? I don't think it will be too hard to find one with the right temperature. In 2013, astronomers estimated that there were eleven billion habitable planets orbiting Sun-like stars."

"What about carbon dioxide atmospheres?" asked Tom.

"Well," answered Helen, "it seems likely that we can find one out of the eleven billion possibilities. Two of the planets in the solar system, Venus and Mars, have atmospheres consisting mostly of carbon dioxide. So, a carbon dioxide atmosphere wouldn't be that unusual."

"OK," said Jackson, "it looks like we have a plan. And we learned something else that will be useful. Shrinking will allow us to time travel more quickly. So, when we don't have any equipment onboard, we can shrink and save screen time."

"I wonder how many other teams have discovered that," I offered.

We spent the next hour putting together the detailed plan for our space station. To give us time to think of any flaws in our plan, we decided to begin the mission two days later, on Saturday. We also made some job assignments. Each of us was tasked with research on the different parts of the space station mission. VC and Johari were going to become the experts at gathering resources for the trip. The rest of the crew was assigned different aspects of the space station construction.

Now I had an even better reason to want to win. I really wanted to beat Milo.

GATHERING RESOURCES

(AS TOLD BY VC)

Johari and I are in charge of gathering resources. We're not actually going to collect them. We are in charge of planning the collection. We need to arrange for food to eat, water to drink, fuel for the ship, oxygen to breathe, and *currency* to buy any equipment that we need. For *currency*, we already have the diamond and geode we collected in Belgium. I got together with Johari on *Room* to plan our collection.

Johari started our discussion. "Hey, VC, what we learned about the time taken by space and time travel could give us a fantastic advantage when it comes to finishing the race with the minimum screen time."

"Right, Jo," I agreed. "We need to keep that in mind as we make plans. We should log on and go to the *Cosmic Egg* so we can check out what extra ship's equipment we might want."

"Hey, VC," Johari said as she scrolled through the catalogue of ship's equipment we could buy. "I think we should get a <u>fusion reactor</u> to power the ship. That runs on hydrogen. We can buy a <u>hydrogen generator</u> that will split water molecules to make hydrogen gas and oxygen gas. So, basically, our fuel will be water. Cool, huh?"

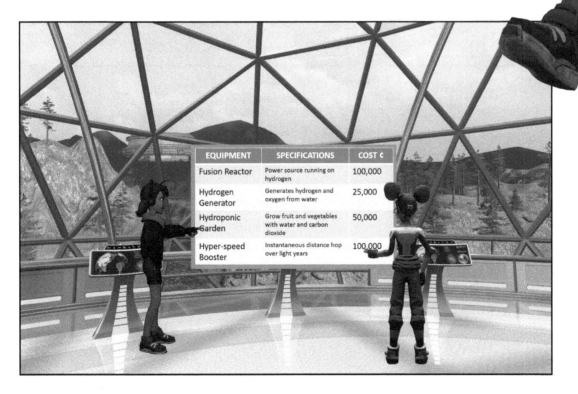

EQUIPMENT	SPECIFICATIONS	COST ¢
Fusion Reactor	Power source running on hydrogen	100,000
Hydrogen Generator	Generates hydrogen and oxygen from water	25,000
Hydroponic Garden	Grow fruit and vegetables with water and carbon dioxide	50,000
Hyper-speed Booster	Instantaneous distance hop over light years	100,000

"OK," I agreed. "That will take care of our oxygen needs too. But we will need a lot more water. We may need a few more comets to mine. Remember when both our teams mined the same comet in *The Stardust Mystery*?" Our teams even had a jumping competition in low gravity, which was extra fun.

"There is one more problem," I pointed out. "It's the ship speed. If we have to travel all over the Milky Way looking for the right planet, it could take forever at the normal ship speed of one million kilometers per second. Even if we could travel at the speed of light, it would take over four years to get to the nearest star."

"How about the *Hyper-Speed Booster* at the bottom of the list?" suggested Johari. "Einstein wouldn't approve of a real object going <u>faster than the speed of light</u>, but this is just a *Virtual World*."

"Yup," I agreed, "let's put that in our plan. I think the diamond we collected in Belgium will cover the cost of those three items."

"Oh, look," Johari said as she scrolled through the equipment list. "You can buy space station modules like on the *International Space Station*. Betcha lots of teams will be doing that."

We continued developing our plan, putting in all the other things we needed to gather. We indicated the years and places where we would find them. When we finished the plan, we called for a meeting to go over it with the team. The other kids reported on their parts of the space station construction. The team approved all the proposals, and we put together a written plan with a diagram.

We were going to be starting the mission tomorrow.

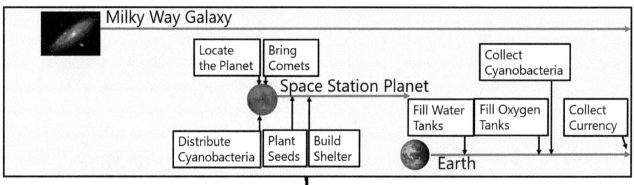

At noon Eastern time, we logged on, went to the *Mystery Museum*, and teleported to the *Cosmic Egg*. It was just the kids this time, no Grandpa or Tom, which was OK, although we could have really used Helen. She is super smart about the evolution of the universe, but she had to teach a class. We wanted to do the first part of our trip at a very small size to save screen time during time travel. Jackson teleported first, and Johari brought up the rear. Unfortunately, Jackson started the size change before Johari was onboard.

"Hey," she yelled through her headset, "I'm still teleporting. Go back to our normal size. I won't fit into that tiny ship you have created."

"Sorry, Jo," Jackson said as he put the ship back to normal size. Johari came onboard, and Jackson said, "I'll keep the size normal until we start serious time travel."

The trip started with full tanks of oxygen and water. Our first task was to increase our *currency* account for things that we might need for our mission. We used the diamond in our account for the initial purchase of the ship's three new equipment items, but Johari and I had identified a diamond mine in Botswana, Africa, where we could add to our *currency* collection. It was one of the largest diamond mines in the world. It was an open pit mine, so we could look for diamonds on the surface.

When we got there, Richie and I grabbed the crystal detectors, which we had also purchased, and teleported to the surface. The other kids joined us too. We searched for twenty minutes and found nothing. I started to worry that we were using too much screen time.

"Hey guys," Jackson called as if he had read my mind. "I think this is a waste of time. I think all the diamonds in areas that have been exposed have all been found. I have a better idea. Let's look for gold instead."

So, Jackson told us about what he had learned in elementary school when he studied California's history. "You guys have heard of the San Francisco 49ers football team, right?" he asked. "Well, the Forty-Niners were actually the people who came to California in the 1849 gold rush. Gold was discovered in 1848 at a place called Sutter's Mill. Lots of gold flakes and nuggets were found in a stream. So, I suggest we go there in 1847, before the gold rush, and pick up some easy change."

It was *California, here we come*. On the way, we ordered a pan that is used for finding the gold in the water. It's called panning for gold. We also ordered a whole bunch of seeds to plant on our *Space Station Planet*. We got seeds for fruit trees and vegetable plants and regular plants too. When we got to northern California, we went back in time to the year 1847. We found the stream at Sutter's Mill and teleported to the surface. Jackson did the panning for gold, and Richie used his trusty detector, set for finding metal.

"Hey, team," shouted Jackson, "look at what I found." He showed us the large gold nugget in his pan.

A little while later, Richie called, "I got one too."

In just one hour, we had collected enough gold to buy almost everything in the ship's catalog. "What's next?" asked Lizzy.

"According to our plan," I answered, "we need to collect the most important thing that will make our *Space Station Planet* livable. We need to collect Grandpa's green slime."

/////

We gathered back aboard the *Cosmic Egg* to start our trip back in time. The first stop was to collect a huge quantity of cyanobacteria (aka green slime), which we were going to use to create an oxygen atmosphere on our *Space Station Planet*. Jackson reduced our size for time travel. That would save screen time. We could reduce our size until the gold filled the equipment room, so we were traveling at just one-thousandth of our normal size. We discovered that the water and oxygen in our tanks would shrink right along with the ship.

"Neddy," I requested, "please keep track of the Earth's oxygen concentration as we go back in time."

Neddy reported that the oxygen concentration was 21% as we started. At one billion years ago, Neddy reported, "The concentration of oxygen is now down to 15%." A little later she announced, "Now it's down to 10%."

"OK," I said, "let's stop here to collect green slime." We were at 1.5 billion years ago.

We traveled around looking for shorelines and swamps that looked green. Every time we found a promising spot, the whole team teleported to the surface and collected the green stuff.

It was kinda hard to breathe because the oxygen concentration was so low. Grandpa had once taken us grandkids on a trek up Mount Ranier. Breathing at the top was difficult then, like it is now. It was hard to work.

We collected green slime in jars and buckets and teleported them to the ship, where the cyanobacteria were sucked into our extra oxygen tank. We went to ten times normal size to increase our holding capacity. We quit when the tank was full. Then we topped off our oxygen tank from Earth's atmosphere. That would be our last chance as there was no oxygen in the atmosphere in the earlier Earth. We topped off our water from a lake.

We reduced our size and started time traveling again. At two billion years ago, Neddy called out, "The atmospheric oxygen just went to zero."

Jackson looked excited. "This must be the start of what Tom called the *Great Oxygen Event*," he said. "That's the start of Earth's period when land creatures that breathe oxygen evolved.

There was already some evolved sealife because the oceans had some oxygen during the previous billion years."

Lizzy added, "Those little green guys get my vote for the heroes of all the animal species. Without them, we wouldn't be here."

We continued back in time. At 4.5 billion years ago, we slowed down and backed away from Earth's surface to watch the formation of the moon playing backwards. A giant asteroid collided with Earth, and a giant chunk flew off to form the moon.

At 4.6 billion years ago, we watched the Earth form in reverse as all the space rocks and gas were pulled together by gravity to form our planet.

Finally, we traveled back to a time before our sun, Earth, and the rest of the solar system planets had formed. The space around us was dark. It was permanent night.

"OK, guys and girls," I announced, "it's time to build our space station."

BUILDING THE PLANET COLORADO SPACE STATION

(AS TOLD BY LIZZY)

This was going to be so way super cool. I thought our genius Idea for the *Space Station Planet* could win it for us in the *Regionals*. I knew it was really important to Johari and Jackson, whose parents were out of work, and to all of us now that there was so much uncertainty.

We had left Planet Earth and the solar system behind, and we were going to search for the right planet to use as our space station. We wanted the right temperature for living and a planet with a carbon dioxide atmosphere that our green slime could convert into a partial oxygen atmosphere.

At eight billion years ago, we'd have to find the perfect planet. Then we needed to find some comets and redirect them to hit our planet to melt and create lakes and oceans. We'd wait a million years for things to settle and then distribute our tank full of green slime.

The next step would be to go ahead by 500 million years and hopefully find we'd created an oxygen atmosphere. Then we could distribute all our seeds, and another 500 million years after that, we would have a beautiful planet with oxygen, water, and vegetation. We'd even have things like virtual apples that we could virtually eat. I don't like fruit, but maybe my avatar will.

When we got to eight billion years ago, still in the Milky Way, I called out, "OK, gang, let's get started."

"I got this," said Jackson. "I'm your planet-finding guy. We are looking for a Sun-like star with a planet at the right distance from it to be at a habitable temperature like we have on Earth. I did my homework, and I found a new study of the data from NASA's Kepler space telescope. The scientists estimated that out of the 100 billion stars in the Milky Way, there are about four billion like our sun. They think that as many as half of them could have habitable planets. That's two billion habitable planets. So, Helen was right, we should be able to find one."

"First we have to locate a Sun-like star," said VC. "That's the job for me and Neddy. We pick a star. I measure the distance to it. She measures the brightness. From that we can determine whether it is like our sun in size."

"Then I use the *Hyper-Speed Booster* to get us there," added Johari. "Then we look for a habitable planet."

"If we find one, then it is my job to check the atmosphere for carbon dioxide," said Richie, proud to have a job to do. "We just keep repeating the process until we find one that is at the right temperature and has carbon dioxide."

Amazingly, on our fifteenth try, we found our planet. We all teleported down to take a look.

When we hit the surface, Richie asked, "What do we need to do to have a party down here?" And answered, "We gotta planet."

"Richie," said Neddy, "the jokes are getting worse and worse. You are embarrassing me because I'm the one that brought you along. Zip it!"

Richie laughed and said, "How do you know God likes Saturn best? He put a ring on it."

"I think this planet is way too rugged," I said, ignoring Richie. "This spot looks like an asteroid hit it."

"Or maybe it's an old volcano," offered VC.

"I like it," added Johari. "It reminds me of our family trip to Colorado. Let's call it *Planet Colorado*."

"Cool with me," I agreed.

"Me too," said Richie, Neddy, and VC.

"*Planet Colorado* it is," said Jackson. "Now we need water. Richie, do a wide search for water out in space. That will help us find comets."

We got back in the *Cosmic Egg* and followed a trail of higher water concentration until we found a comet. "I have a better plan than trying to tow it," advised Jackson.

He did some calculations of the comet's trajectory and then said, "Lizzy, do a twenty-four-hour time freeze on the comet. That should change its course enough so that it will hit *Planet Colorado*. It should hit in about one year. Let's go back to the planet to make sure it does."

So we did a one-year time hop and went back to our planet. The impact occurred right on schedule. *Planet Colorado* had its first dose of water.

"OK," said Jackson, "now let's repeat the process."

We found and redirected twenty more large comets. We decided that was enough.

"Let's go forward one million years." I said. "Things should have settled down by then from the comet impacts. Then we can add our green slime."

We flew over the planet shorelines as we dumped the cyanobacteria from our tank. Then we advanced 500 million years to see if we had an oxygen atmosphere. Richie checked and reported, "Looks like we've got about 20% oxygen in the atmosphere already." We high fived. "The rest is mostly carbon dioxide. Come on, Dee, let's teleport down and make sure we can breathe."

Richie and Neddy went down to the surface and took off their helmets. "All OK," Neddy told us. Then she added, "Send down some seeds for trees and flowers for us to plant artistically."

Jackson and VC went down to the surface with seeds to help with the planting. Johari and I flew the *Cosmic Egg* around the planet, letting seeds fly over the land.

We finished planting and distributing our load of seeds. Then we advanced another ten million years to see how we had done.

We all teleported to the surface to see the results. Trees made tall, beautiful forests. There were even a few lakes. I thought I heard something that sounded like a bug buzz by my face.

"Beautiful," I said. "The *Planet Colorado Space Station*. This is the GOAT, to use Johari's favorite expression."

Richie checked the oxygen concentration in the atmosphere. It was now 24%.

"Our plan worked perfectly," VC bragged. "There is a breathable atmosphere, a river, and plants have grown."

"This is so beautiful that I might want to live here permanently," said Johari.

"What did Earth say to the other planets?" Richie asked, but this time he said it with breathless wonder while looking around at what we'd done. "You gotta get a life."

"It is great," I agreed. "But we need one final touch. We need a headquarters building."

"But we don't have any building materials for an HQ," objected Johari.

"Yes, we do," answered VC. "Let's clone the *Cosmic Egg*. We can use the flight deck with the top half of the bubble. It will provide lights and heat and a roof over our heads. And the cloned fusion reactor will be our power source."

It only took us a few minutes to make our *Cosmic Egg*-clone HQ.

We flew the drone out to take a picture of the *Planet Colorado Space Station* with the *Cosmic Egg* hovering overhead. We emailed it to Grandpa, Helen, and Tom.

"I think it is a winner," I offered. Everyone agreed.

"OK, guys," I said, "remember, we have to measure the distance to *Andromeda* for Professor Lemaître."

So Neddy and Jackson set to work doing the measurements.

"Professor Lemaître is going to love this," announced Jackson. "The distance to *Andromeda* is now only 77% of what it is in the present time."

"Looks like his <u>Hypothesis of the Cosmic Egg</u>, aka *The Big Bang*, is correct," said Johari. And that theory really is the GOAT."

Planet Colorado Space Station

"Let's head to seven billion years ago to complete the mission," said Neddy.

"I have a better idea," I suggested. "We really finished all our tasks. Why don't we save time and just head home?"

So, we reduced our size to save travel time back to the present and headed for home.

We will find out who wins on June 30. It is going to be a long week.

Our decision to skip the stop at seven billion years ago would prove to have both good and bad consequences.

16

JUDGING THE SPACE STATIONS

(AS TOLD BY MILO)

The news about the three winners in our region arrived by FedEx on July 4, right on schedule. It announced that my team, the *Space Pioneers*, was one of the three *Northeast Regionals* winners! That meant we made it into the *Finals*. Awesome! And, no surprise, my old team, the *Cosmic Explorers*, was one of the other *Northeast Regionals* winners too. It said that there would be a meeting on July 15 to find out who won the *Regionals* top prize of $25,000.

Because of the pandemic and all the travel restrictions, the meeting to judge the space stations looked like it was going to be virtual. But in July, the Covid-19 infection rate was dropping rapidly, and the situation in California was pretty good.

On July 7, TSI sent emails to tell everyone their decision. The US contestants could come to California in person if they could do it safely. All others in the United States and those from abroad would attend online. All in-person meetings would be held outdoors.

My team had decided to make the trip. On the almost-empty plane, Svetlana and I were sitting with an unoccupied seat between us. We wore double masks. The rest of my new team was close by. Of course, everyone onboard was wearing facemasks, and there were seats between any people who didn't ask to sit together. It looked weird.

What really made me miserable was that my old team that I deserted was on the plane too. They were about ten rows in front of me. I had hoped I wouldn't have to face them.

We were landing in thirty minutes. I would try to avoid my family when I got off the plane and get into a different car when we were taken to the TSI mansion on the ocean south of San Fransisco. But, eventually, I was going to have to face them. I felt terrible about leaving the *Cosmic Explorers*, but I was going to feel even worse if they beat my new team.

I thought our idea for the space station was brilliant. Svetlana and I and her family did a big brainstorming session. Our ideas bounced back and forth. We knew we needed to build something awesome without using a lot of screen time. We knew that parts from the *International Space Station* were available in the catalog. But traveling back and forth to seven billion years ago with all the parts for a complete space station would suck up too much screen time. My awesome suggestion was that if we could clone some of our spaceship's parts instead, we could keep the travel down to just one trip.

We ended up cloning the flight deck with the bubble enclosure, water tank, and oxygen tank. We purchased solar panels for power.

Here's a picture of the *Space Pioneer Station* outside our ship with me, Svetlana, and Natasha inside. You can see why I had trouble telling the two of them apart.

Our project took just one round trip to seven billion years ago. So our total screen time was just four hours of travel plus one hour for the cloning and assembly—only five hours of total screen time.

After we landed, I couldn't avoid the *Cosmic Explorers* at the baggage carousel. G-pa and Richie said hi, and G-pa did an elbo bump with me, which made me feel good. Lizzy, Neddy, and VC glared at me. I got into a different car with my team for the ride to the TSI mansion, so I didn't have to talk to them after that.

▰ ▰ ▰ ▰ ▰

At the mansion, while waiting to check in, I heard Richie talking to my cousins.

"This place is so cool," he said. "I've never been to California. The ocean on one side of us and the huge, snow-covered mountains on the other are amazing. They call the little hills in Connecticut mountains." Pointing out the window, he said, "*Those* are mountains."

"Wait till you see the rest of the mansion," said Neddy, who had been here last year for the *Science and the Future Contest*. "Everything is way modern. Last year, we got taken to Disneyland and had a Zero-G plane ride. I wonder what we'll get to do this year."

Jackson, Johari, and an adult, that I am guessing was their dad, were also checking in. I bet they drove up from Los Angeles.

"This is really the GOAT for you guys," said Johari, who was masked and talking to Richie. "But Jackson and I live in California. It's not so unusual for us."

When they turned to go to their rooms, I got the icy stare again. This visit was not going to be fun if this continued. After we checked in, I went to find Lizzy to try to explain why I left our team. I found her out on the balcony, looking at the ocean.

"Hi, Lizzy," I said. "Can we talk?"

"Oh," she responded, without turning to look at me, "if it isn't *Milo the Missing*. Not missing anymore. What is there to talk about?"

"I want to explain why I left you guys," I answered. She stiffened, put her hands on her hips, and continued staring out at the ocean. "Oh, congratulations on the *Cosmic Explorers* being finalists in the *Regionals*. I knew you would."

"Thanks," Lizzy huffed. "Congratulations to you guys too."

"Here's the thing," I started. "Svetlana and I are really close. I was taking up so much time with you and the contest . . . I really missed her. Then, when I saw her, it was hard keeping our stuff secret from her because it's all we wanted to talk about. So, I begged her to join *our* team, but she said she couldn't desert her family. So, the only solution I could think of was for *me* to join *hers*."

"But then you were deserting *your* family," Lizzy argued.

"Yes, that's true," I answered. "And I am really sorry about that. But you guys have this incredible team: G-pa, Tom, Helen, Neddy, Johari, and the *Boy Genius*. Svetlana would be deserting the family that she actually lives with, and she only had her sisters and brother. Even their scientist was hardly ever around. They needed me. You guys didn't. What I am truly sorry and embarrassed about is that I didn't have the courage to tell you all in person or at least in a *Room* meeting. I was being a coward. Please forgive me."

I could see her body starting to relax a little. She took her hands off her hips and turned to look at me. "OK," she said, "I understand. You're right. It would have been really awkward having you on our team with you spending all your other time with Svetlana. I forgive you. But you need to talk to the rest of the team. Just know that we will be fighting as hard as we can to beat you. Not Svetlana. Not Natasha. *You*. Good luck." She turned and walked off the balcony, leaving me alone to stare at the ocean.

Later, I found my family together on the patio and explained my decision to them. I hoped the icy stares would stop now.

▟ ▟ ▟ ▟ ▟

The activity that TSI had planned for us on this trip was even more awesome than last year's excursions. We went whale watching. We only saw some fins in the distance for most of the morning.

"This isn't fun," complained Richie. "I wanna see some whales up close."

Just then, a huge whale jumped out of the water right in front of us. Richie was so shocked that he fell backward onto his butt.

I had my camera ready for

just such a scene and snapped the picture. It will be my entry for G-pa's July photo contest, which G-pa says I can definitely still be a part of. He said I could invite Svetlana and her family to enter pictures too.

After we came back from the whale watch, Svetlana and I took a long walk on the beach. It was beautiful. The sounds came from the waves crashing on the shore and the seagulls calling each other. We ran into G-pa and my cousins, also walking the beach. Neddy agreed with me when I said the whale watch was way cool. The icy stares seemed to be mostly gone.

▟ ▟ ▟ ▟ ▟

That afternoon, we gathered outside on the patio, which was set up like an auditorium with a stage. We were going to hear each team give a presentation about its space station. Everyone wore face masks and sat socially-distanced. The new president of TSI, Dr. Quinna Quixote, was the MC. Everyone called her Doctor Quinna so as not to confuse her with her brother, Quentin Quixote, known as Dr. Q. The three winners in each region took turns onstage describing their space station entries. They started alphabetically with Australia and then Bangladesh, both presenting remotely. A bajillion years later, it finally came time for the three United States *Northeast Regionals* winners. I represented the *Space Pioneers*, Lizzy represented the *Cosmic Explorers*, and a guy named Kaito Matsuo from Vermont represented the *Northern Warriors*. Each of us was supposed to describe our space station construction and how it would provide the resources we needed for exploring space and time. It was supposed to be a place where we could replenish our food, oxygen, water, and fuel.

I went first. I described how we cloned our ship's flight deck and enclosure for the main space station module. "Using a clone for the main part of the construction allowed us to build our station with only a single trip back to seven billion years ago," I said. "That saved screen time." I went on to explain how our travel and construction time total was just five hours, and we only had to transport the solar panels for power and a hydroponic garden for food. I told everyone how we left one of our full water tanks at the space station.

Doctor Quinna asked if there were any questions.

One kid raised her hand and asked, "The hydroponic garden takes a lot of water and oxygen. How will you supply that when the tanks run out?"

"We have a plan for that," I answered. "We can mine comet ice for water. We purchased the oxygen/hydrogen generator for the space station. That will allow us to split water into oxygen and hydrogen to provide extra oxygen."

There were no more questions.

Kaito of the *Northern Warriors* went next. "We purchased both the *International Space Station*'s main module and the solar panels, so it took us two trips to build our space station. Our total screen time was nine hours. We had the same plan as the *Space Pioneers* for extra resources. We purchased the hydroponic garden and oxygen/hydrogen generator, and we will use comet mining for extra water and oxygen."

There were no questions for Kaito.

Then Lizzy and the *Cosmic Explorers* were up. "The idea for our space station came from our youngest team member, Richie Torres." I was amazed as Lizzy shared the idea to build their station using resources found back in time. Richie never seemed that smart to me, but here he was, proving me wrong.

"So, we traveled back to eight billion years ago," Lizzy explained. "We located a planet with a Sun-like star that had a habitable temperature like Earth and a carbon dioxide atmosphere. The planet had rugged mountains and valleys like Colorado. Then we found comets. We changed the comet orbits so that they would crash into our planet and provide it with water for lakes and oceans. We went forward a million years in time to let things settle and added a secret ingredient that we had brought with us. We dumped our secret ingredient all over the planet. Then we went forward in time by 500 million years, and our secret ingredient had created a partial oxygen atmosphere. We planted and distributed the seeds we had brought for trees, including fruit trees, and plants, including vegetables."

"Then," Lizzy continued, "we jumped ahead 10 million years to see what we had created. Our plan was a success. We had our beautiful *Planet Colorado*. To complete the space station, we cloned the upper half of our ship's enclosure for our headquarters. We cloned our fusion reactor for power. Hydrogen for the fusion reactor would be obtained from water using our oxygen/hydrogen generator."

In conclusion, Lizzy said, "The *Planet Colorado Space Station* was finished and running, so we returned to the present. We used a total of 3.5 hours of screen time for travel and construction."

Sitting in the audience, Svetlana raised her hand and asked, "What was the secret ingredient?"

Lizzy answered, "Something called green slime, also known as cyanobacteria."

I knew that had to be G-pa's idea.

"We collected it from Earth at 1.5 billion years ago," explained Lizzy. "When Earth first formed, it had no oxygen in the atmosphere. It was the green slime that added the oxygen gas. It converted carbon dioxide to oxygen and water by photosynthesis. The atmospheric oxygen is what allowed animal life to evolve on Earth. I believe pond scum deserves way more respect than we give it."

Natasha asked, "How did you do the whole thing in just 3.5 hours? The round-trip travel time to seven billion years ago alone is 4 hours. It doesn't make sense."

"We figured out a way to do that," said Lizzy. "Doctor Quinna, we would like to keep that a secret. Is that OK?"

Much to my disappointment, Doctor Quinna said it was OK. I knew I had to figure out how they did it before we did our missions for the *Finals*.

There were no further questions, and the three of us left the stage.

The last teams in the regions from the United States made their presentations. Then Doctor Quinna came onstage and made an announcement. "The judges will review all of the space stations that you terrific kids have presented. Tomorrow at dinner, the winners in each region and the top winner for all the regions will be announced. Thank you all for a job well done. Enjoy tonight's dinner."

We had dinner on the patio. Then we left and found things to do. I am guessing that Lizzy and Jackson resumed their gin rummy game.

Svetlana and I went for a night walk along the ocean.

▬ ▬ ▬ ▬ ▬

The morning was beautiful, sunny, and warm. It was definitely a beach day. It looked like every single team was there, sunning, swimming, walking, running, and playing ball. Everyone was socially distanced, though, which was cool. We all knew how bad that virus could be because of what we'd seen G-pa go through. I watched Jackson do his juggling thing. He could now juggle five balls at once.

Like last year, G-pa was giving body-surfing lessons. But this year, he had about thirty people in his class. There were kids and grownups from all over the United States trying to catch the big waves.

Doctor Quinna had sandwiches, fruit, and drinks sent down to the beach at lunchtime, so we didn't even have to leave. It was an awesome day.

At 5:00 p.m. we went back to the mansion to clean up. At 6:00, we were back on the patio, which was set up for dinner.

There was a big surprise when G-ma sat down next to G-pa at the table that the *Space Pioneers* were sharing with the *Cosmic Explorers*.

"I'm not letting Grandpa have all the fun," she said, laughing. "I was not going to miss this."

I was surprised because G-ma was taking Covid really seriously, and she didn't want to fly. I guess she changed her mind. But, as G-pa said, we all still have to live our lives, even if we have to be careful. The second big surprise was that the first course was G-ma's famous Chinese dumplings. She told me she was there in the morning and had supervised the kitchen staff in preparing them. G-ma rules. Awesome!

Dinner was delicious.

Before dessert, both Dr. Q and Doctor Quinna walked onstage and tapped the microphone for quiet. "The judges have reviewed all the wonderful space stations," Dr. Q. announced. "They have made their decisions."

"The winner in the Australian region is the *Kangaroo Kids,*" announced Doctor Quinna. "The winner in the Bangladeshi region is . . ." Doctor Quinna went through the alphabet of regions. Dr. Q took over at Norway. It seemed like forever before he got to regions in the United States.

I expected the winner to be the *Cosmic Explorers*. They had a really unusual solution that had all the resources, and they created their space station in the shortest time of any team.

Dr. Q announced, "The winner of the *Northeast Region* of the United States is . . . the *Cosmic Explorers*!"

G-ma and G-pa did the hugs and kisses thing with my cousins, but they elbow bumped Johari and Jackson. Me and my team congratulated them. After a bunch more announcements, it was time to announce the overall winner for the big prize of $25,000.

Doctor Quinna took the microphone. "The winner is," and the sound of a fanfare came over the loudspeakers, "the *Cosmic Explorers.*"

G-pa, G-ma, and the *Cosmic Explorers* erupted into cheers, shouting and elbow bumping. Even the *Space Pioneers* were happy that at least the winning team was from our region. The *Cosmic Explorers* ran up onstage and accepted congratulations and a big, fat check from Dr. Q. There were speeches by Dr. Q. and Doctor Quinna. Jackson spoke for the *Cosmic Explorers*, thanking our hosts and saying how much fun the contest was. Everyone came back to our table for dessert of chocolate lava cake, which was awesome!

I was disappointed, but honestly, I knew how good it was that they'd won. And, anyway, I was pretty sure Svet and I, with our little team, could win the cool mil!

When dinner and the other contest announcements were finally over, lots of the other team members came over to congratulate the *Cosmic Explorers*.

G-pa said, "I'm going to call Tom and tell him the good news. Jackson, you should call Helen. Kids, you should call your parents and tell them."

There were lots of conversations as people milled about until ten o'clock. Then we all said our goodbyes.

Early the next morning, everyone headed to the airport. On our flight home, I was thinking what a jerk I was for leaving the winning team. But I forgot that as soon as I looked at Svet, and she smiled her beautiful smile at me.

There was still the *Finals* to be won. And if anyone can win, it's us.

PART 4
THE FINALS
(MID-JULY TO AUGUST)

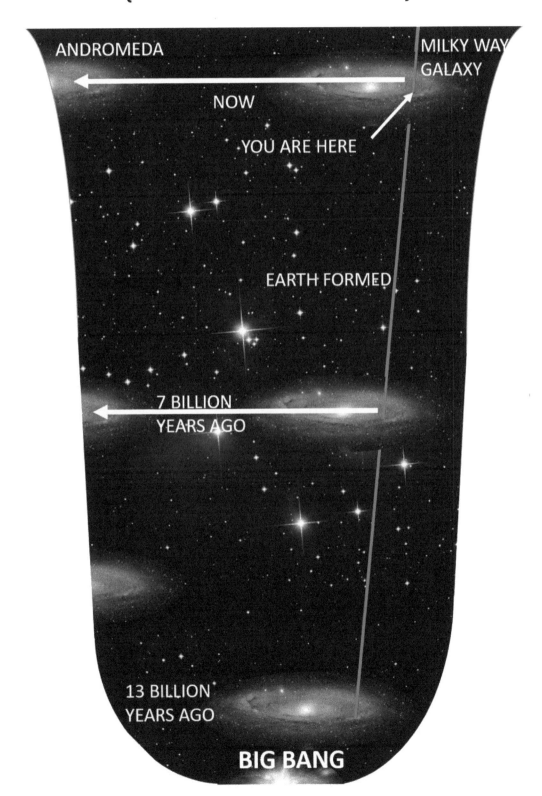

17

THE FINALS BEGIN

(AS TOLD BY NEDDY)

Lizzy and I are back home after our amazing trip to California. We won the *Region-als* grand prize. We have Richie to thank for that. So lucky. Most of the *Regionals* winners built their space stations using modules based on the ones used for the *International Space Station*. The parts were available in the ship's catalog.

Five teams, including our team and Milo's team, figured out that they could save travel time by cloning their ship's parts instead. But our team, the *Cosmic Explorers*, was the only team that decided to build our space station on a planet! Everyone is talking about how way cool the *Planet Colorado Space Station* is. I definitely agree.

The meeting in California was a wonderful break from our pandemic lockdown routines, but now the routines are back. Dad seems to have completely recovered from his Covid-19 infection, but he and Mom are still not back to work at the University of Connecticut. They stopped getting paid in June, and I have heard them discussing what they are going to do if they don't start teaching again in the fall.

Lizzy is going to call a *Room* meeting with everyone for noon today to discuss our plans for the *Finals*. We also have to decide how we will share the $25,000 prize that we won.

Lizzy and I started the meeting at five of twelve, and by five after, everyone was present.

Grandpa started it off. "I want to tell you kids how proud I am of your success in the contest. Winning the *Regionals* among the hundreds of teams that you beat is amazing. You all did a spectacular job."

Tom agreed. "You kids are very special. I am proud to be working with you."

"Me too," added Helen. "Wonderful job."

"I have some interesting news," I reported. "My dad showed me an article that announced our win in the *Hartford Times*. It had our names in it and told all about our space station. The mayor of West Hartford was quoted as saying we were lucky to have such smart kids in our city. Then she wished us luck in the *Finals*."

"The Los Angeles paper had an article too," Johari added. "We're famous!"

"Well," added Jackson, "the $1 million grand prize should have lots of people covering the contest."

"Hey, everyone," announced Grandpa, "There's a great picture in the *Hartford Times* article showing all of us onstage in California receiving our award. There's a picture of the *Planet Colorado Space Station* on the screen. The *Planet Colorado* picture must be from a screenshot you took when you were there, because three of you kids are in it."

We all talked over each other about the very cool press coverage, and then Grandpa got all of our attention again. "What shall I do with this check that I have for $25,000?"

"We should divide it among the kids," Tom suggested. "You kids did almost all of the work."

"No," argued Lizzy, "you adults were important too. I think it should be shared equally."

"I have a suggestion," I offered. "Lots of our parents are out of work. Why don't we put the winnings in a bank account and let anyone's parents or any adults in the group take money from it if they need it to get through the hard times."

Grandpa nodded seriously, and I could tell he liked my idea, which felt great. "Yes," he agreed. "And once the pandemic is over, we will split whatever remains among the rest of us."

Everyone liked the idea, so it was agreed.

Helen commented that the Covid-19 cases were starting to rise in Southern California, and asked Jackson, "How are you and your family doing?"

"Well," answered Jackson, "no one has gotten sick, but Dad is still out of work. We may want to take advantage of that bank account, but I think my dad will want it to be a loan."

"We can worry about that later," Grandpa said. "For now, the money will be made available as needed to all the grownups."

"Anyway," Lizzy called out, almost pushing me over to get her giant head on my screen, "pretty soon we'll win that million dollars, and everyone will forget about a measly twenty-five grand!"

We all hooted and cheered. It was so exciting.

That got us down to the business of discussing how we were going to win the *Finals*. We had an advantage. We had the lowest amount of screen time used so far among all the competing teams, and we had our secret about how to minimize time-travel time for the *Finals*: shrinking our ship.

"Here is what we need to do for the *Finals*," I said looking at the printout of the rules. "It looks like there are five parts. Part **One**, we need to choose and tell the story of *The Five Most Unusual Things in the Universe.*

"Part **Two**," continued my sister, who grabbed the printout from me, "we need to find the source of our stardust, our own atoms. We need to travel to the time and places where they were created and take screenshots of the events."

"Part **Three**," called out VC who had a copy of the printout as well, "we have a bunch of things to find in the time period from the present to 7 billion years ago. It's like a space/time scavenger hunt."

Part **Four** was described by Johari, which was that we had to do a similar scavenger hunt for the period between 7 billion years ago and the Big Bang.

Then for part **Five**, Jackson read, "We need to go back to the *Big Bang* and actually build the first atoms in the universe. I will be happy to be in charge of that."

"We need to plan carefully so we keep our screen time to a minimum," Johari reminded us. "We don't want to go back and forth in time."

"That's right," I said. "So keep screen time in mind as we choose *The Five Most Unusual Things in the Universe*. Also, remember to be careful when using the *Cosmic Egg*. If we crash it or destroy it in any way, our team is disqualified. We'd be out of the contest! So who's going to lead part **One**?"

"I'll take charge of part **One**," Johari offered. "Let's put together a list of the most unusual things. Please email me with your suggestions. Helen, Tom, and Grandpa, this is where we really need your input. I'll assemble all the suggestions, and we can choose the top five."

We then assigned the leaders for parts **Two**, **Three**, and **Four**. We were ready to end the meeting when Johari said, "Hey guys, let me show you my August entry for Grandpa's photo contest." Johari did a screen share with a picture of sea lions napping on the beach instead of on a bench. "I ran into them when we took a trip up the coast past Malibu."

"I have a picture too," said VC. "It's of six turtles all lined up on a floating log. Cool, huh?"

"But I have the winner," bragged Richie. "I was hiking with my little brother, Leo, and we spotted a cave. I started to go in, but then this monster creature started coming out. Leo snapped this picture just before we started to run like crazy."

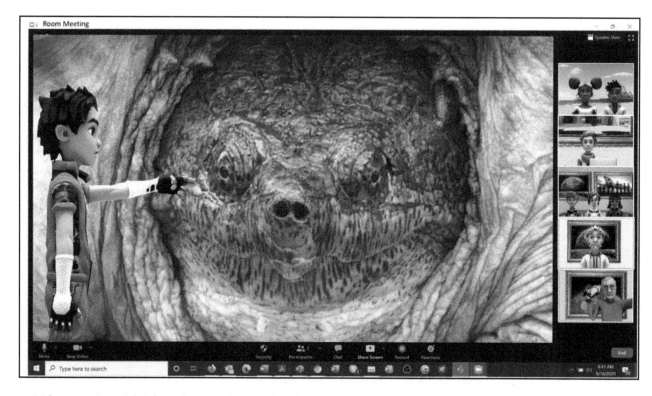

"Oh, man," I said, "that thing is big and ugly. What is it? You must have been really scared."

"Wait just a minute," demanded Lizzy. "I don't believe there is such a creature. I think you Photo-shopped the picture."

Then Richie started laughing and admitted it was a fake. "OK, guys, you got me. It was just a close-up of the face of a normal-size turtle. Here is what it looked like." He screen-shared to show us the real thing. "I want to submit the turtle face for the August contest."

With no more pictures to share, and our assignments made for the *Finals*, we ended the meeting.

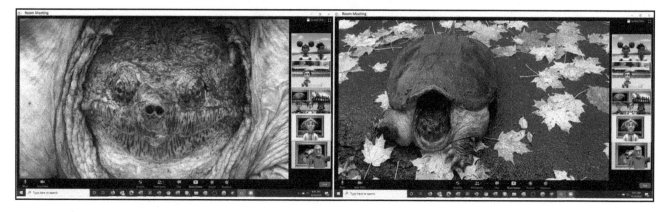

THE FIVE MOST UNUSUAL THINGS IN THE UNIVERSE

(AS TOLD BY JOHARI)

There was lots of excitement when Jack and I got home from the *Regionals* awards meeting. The $25,000 grand-prize award got us a front-page story in our local newspaper. Mom and Dad were overjoyed, and lots of friends called to congratulate us and ask about our experience.

I went back to my way of keeping my head clear by running on the beach. I was still taking singing lessons, so I sang as I ran. Dad was still bummed about being out of work because of the pandemic, so sometimes he came running with me. I liked that a lot.

I had offered to do the job coordinating our team's list and stories for *The Five Most Unusual Things in the Universe*. This job was not going to be easy. We were going to be judged on our choices and how we illustrated and explained the unusual things. We needed to keep our screen time to a minimum too, so it was very important that we made a really good list. I got emails from the rest of the team with their suggestions.

Helen's email arrived first. It had one really unusual thing: the dwarf planet Haumea. It was a funny-looking, egg-shaped planet with rings and two moons. It rotated really fast, so it only had a 4.5-hour-long day. Helen had a bunch of other suggestions too, and I got lots more from the other team members.

I made a single list combining the suggestions for unusual things in the universe and emailed it to the team. I scheduled a *Room* meeting to discuss the list and put them in order of popularity. We logged onto *Room* for the meeting. But before we could start on the list, Lizzy announced, "Hey team, TSI just put up the first leaderboard based on the *Regionals* judging." Everyone got the leaderboard up on their computers, and the *Cosmic Explorers* were number one.

"Super," said Jackson. "It looks like we're in first place because of our minimum screen time."

"I looked at the notes for the scoring," added Lizzy. "We got a bonus of one hour because we were the grand-prize winners in the *Regionals*. We get to subtract the bonus hour from the screen time. The winners in each local region got bonuses too, but just a half hour."

Time & Space Inc.

BEST INVENTION: THE COSMIC KIDS

Cosmic Explorers

THE LEADERBOARD FOR JULY 15

TEAM	% OF RACE COMPLETED	SCREEN TIME HRS USED	BONUS TIME AWARDS (HRS)
COSMIC EXPLORERS	0%	3.5	-1.0
AUSSIE ASTRONAUTS	0%	4.5	-0.5
JAPAN JOURNEYERS	0%	4.5	-0.5
THE SMASH	0%	4.5	-0.5
TIME TRAVELERS	0%	4.5	-0.5
EINSTEIN'S GIRLS	0%	4.5	-0.5
ENGLISH EXPLORERS	0%	4.5	-0.5
THE WOW	0%	4.6	0
SPANISH SPRINTERS	0%	4.7	0
SPACE PIONEERS	0%	5.0	0

CONTEST NEWS: The Cosmic Explorers start the Finals Race to the Big Bang as the team with the lowest screen time used to build their Planet Colorado Space Station, which won the Regionals grand prize. Congratulations.

"No bonus for Milo's *Space Pioneers*," observed Neddy. "Too bad."

"Yeah," Lizzy agreed smiling enormously, "too bad, so sad!" She definitely didn't mean it.

We finally got down to sorting through all the suggestions. Our top five choices were:

1. Planet Earth with its human inhabitants
2. The *Twin Paradox* of Einstein's *Theory of Relativity*
3. Black holes that eat stars
4. Gravitational waves
5. Dark matter that may have killed the dinosaurs

Neddy and VC were going to research how humans came to be on Planet Earth. Lizzy and Neddy would cover the *Twin Paradox*, which was annoying to Jackson and me because we actually were the twins. But Jackson and I were going to get to look into black holes that eat stars, which was, I'm happy to say, the *coolest* one. Then Lizzy, VC, and I would take on gravitational waves.

There were other suggestions that didn't make the top five, like Helen's egg-shaped planet, which I personally loved, but it was at the bottom of the list.

We worked individually and in small teams to put our five stories together. Then we submitted them to Grandpa, Tom, and Helen for suggested changes. Final drafts were reviewed by the whole team and we completed all the suggested edits.

"Remember," cautioned Lizzy, "when you are using the *Cosmic Egg*, don't do anything that could put the ship in danger. Destroying the ship could get us disqualified."

We paid attention to ship safety as we carried out our plans.

These are the stories that came from our adventures.

◢◢◢◢◢

UNUSUAL PLANET EARTH

BY

NEDDY AND VC (AS TOLD BY NEDDY)

Just imagine that you are a space explorer from another galaxy. You have traveled to the Milky Way galaxy and find a smallish star. You explore the star's planets and find lights coming out from the planet's surface.

"That's strange," you say. "Where are these lights coming from?"

You go down closer to investigate the source of the light. It does not look like any other planet that you have ever seen. There are structures that look like they have been built, and there is light coming from the structures. Then you see things flying in the sky, and these have blinking lights. Some of them land on areas with lights all around the edges. You circle the planet, heading for daylight created by the nearby sun, and you find this strange sight: funny little rectangular objects flow like blood cells through what look like arteries.

You've explored other planets of other stars. They are nothing like this. This is surely one of the most unusual things in the universe.

"This, of course, is our Planet Earth," I said. "It started out much like the desolate planet Mars, but something peculiar happened 3.7 billion years ago. Grandpa's green slime (cyanobacteria) or other similar single-celled organisms appeared on Earth. These organisms were capable of using carbon dioxide in the atmosphere to grow and to release oxygen. They used sunlight in a process called photosynthesis. The cells could also make exact copies of themselves using an amazing molecule called DNA, and sometimes altered copies of the DNA appeared, called mutations. These altered copies would sometimes become unique organisms."

"Over billions of years," continued VC, "in a process called <u>evolution</u>, the single-celled organisms became cell colonies, and then multicelled organisms with ever-improving capabilities. Evolution depended on those alterations of the DNA. Eventually, a variety of large and small egg-laying dinosaurs evolved to rule the Earth. Small mammals were there too. They made their homes underground to stay safely away from the fierce dinosaurs."

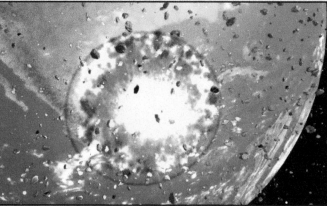

Scenes from the science video, "The Stardust Mystery Online Introduction."
the STARDUST MYSTERY YouTube Channel

"But then," I added, "something awesome happened 65 million years ago to change the fate of the mammals. A huge asteroid hit Planet Earth. It caused the atmosphere to heat up to pizza-oven temperatures. All the land dinosaurs died, but some mammals, including the small mammals from which humans eventually evolved, survived in the cooler temperature of their underground homes. Yay, mammals!"

"Mammals became bigger," continued VC, "and took over the rule of Planet Earth. Millions of years later, humans appeared. During a very brief 200,000 years, humans figured out how to build structures filled with lights, like those first seen by our space explorers. They also created those vehicles that flowed like blood cells through arteries, actually cars on roads built to help humanity travel and cover the globe."

Humans have complex thoughts and emotions. They developed art and science and have organized cities, societies, and governments. They built telescopes and satellites that can see events that happened over 13 billion years ago, and they can predict events well into the future. Some of them even visited the moon. Humans sifted through the history laid down in Earth's rocks to find the evidence of the asteroid impact that killed the dinosaurs. They discovered the story of the *Big Bang*, which started the universe 13.8 billion years ago. They developed the science of medicine and unraveled the mysteries of DNA.

They are the first species that we know of that can actually change their own evolution and the evolution of the species around them by modifying their DNA. Humans have the power to repair damage and help create a sustainable future, not just for themselves but for many other species on their planet.

Such a history seems so improbable that Planet Earth must be very unusual. After listening to the radio waves from outer space and looking over research amassed by some of the greatest space programs in the world, it would appear that no planet nearby contains intelligent life.

VC, the rest of the *Cosmic Explorers,* and I nominate Planet Earth, with its humans, as the number-one most unusual thing in the universe.

THE TWIN PARADOX
BY
LIZZY, NEDDY, AND GRANDPA (AS TOLD BY GRANDPA)

Here's our fantastic story. It starts in 1905, the year Albert Einstein published his *Special Theory of Relativity*. His famous equation $E = mc^2$ came from that theory. It predicted that mass, like a chunk of uranium or a cloud of hydrogen, could be turned into energy. That is the basis for the energy from the sun, atomic power plants, and nuclear weapons.

But there were other strange predictions that stretched our imaginations. Einstein said that the speed of light was always a constant. Lizzy liked that one. "Think of this experiment," proposed Lizzy. "Neddy, have a pitcher throw her fastball to you as you stand in a speeding convertible. Do it when your car is moving toward her. Then do the same thing when your car is moving away. Which pitch will appear faster to you?"

"That's easy," answered Neddy. "The pitch when you are speeding toward her will appear faster. Just imagine it: you are moving toward the ball at the same time as the ball is moving toward you. It's a no-brainer."

"Right," said Lizzy. "The pitch speed *plus* the speed of the car is the first measurement. The pitch speed *minus* the speed of the car is the second. Now think about the speed of light that is coming to you from a star as the Earth is moving *toward* the star. How does that compare to the speed of light from the same star as the Earth is moving *away* from the star? You'd think the light-speed measurements would be different by twice the speed of the Earth moving through space."

"But that's not true," I corrected. "The speed of light is the same no matter where the light comes from or how fast you are moving toward or away from it."

"And then there was this weird thing about the mass or weight of an object," Lizzy continued. "Imagine you cranked the speed of a spaceship up to nearly the speed of light. The mass of the ship would become larger and larger as it approached light speed. It would become infinitely large at the speed of light. Based on that, Einstein made another hypothesis: objects cannot go faster than the speed of light."

"Time clocks also get weird when they're in motion," added Neddy. "If that speeding spaceship had a clock onboard that you could see from the ground, it would look like the clock was going slower than your clock on the ground that was standing still. That is what the *Twin Paradox* is all about. If I am on the ground and my twin is in the spaceship, my twin wouldn't be getting older as fast as me because her clock is going slower."

Neddy and Lizzy decided to test that strange prediction.

"We'll use the *Virtual World* and the *Cosmic Egg*," suggested Neddy. "You take a trip to the nearest star. Do it at nine-tenths the speed of light. You circle the star and then come back to Earth."

"OK," agreed Lizzy. "I just looked it up. The nearest star to Earth is Proxima Centauri. It is 4.25 light years away. If I go at 0.9 times the speed of light, the round trip is going to take me nine and a half years."

"What are you going to do while I'm gone?" asked Lizzy.

"I plan to hang out in the *Virtual World* doing fun stuff," said Neddy. "First, I am going to New York City to shop for clothes and see a Broadway musical. Then I'll go to school and work on getting into college. By the time you get back, I'll be almost 10 years older. Maybe I'll get married.

"Oh," Neddy continued, "while you are at Proxima Centauri, check around to see if you see any planets with lights on them at night. See if you detect any radio signals that might be coming from intelligent life. That will help confirm whether Earth really is unusual. Let's plan for half a year for you to explore the Proxima Centauri star system, so 10 years total. Let's meet back at the *Mystery Museum* on August 1, 2030.

"The most important thing is this," continued Neddy. "If Einstein was correct, and the *Virtual World* has the physics programmed correctly, I will be the older sister when you come back. Your clock will be slower because you acceler-ated to nearly the speed of light and then slowed down when you got home. I'd so love being the older sister for once."

"That sounds crazy," said Lizzy, "but if this works, it will certainly be one of the *Five Most Unusual Things in the Universe*."

They checked with me and the rest of the team. We approved their plan. They were good to go.

Lizzy and Neddy logged on to the *Virtual World*. They could see the *Mystery Museum* through the trees at the end of the road where they had spawned in. They ran to the entrance and went inside.

"OK, Neddy," said Lizzy, "have a nice life while I am gone." Lizzy did something she almost never does; she gave Neddy a sisterly hug. Neddy looked at her with total shock as Lizzy teleported to the *Cosmic Egg*.

■■■■■

The girls kept their *Virtual World* session going with their avatars each doing their thing. We got ready for the next part of the plan, where I, who had come to their house, was going to join them. I logged into the same *Virtual World* session that the girls had started, and Neddy and Lizzy logged on for a second time. We all walked to the Mystery Museum and went to the large meeting room. We were in the present time, August 1, 2020, so the girls' first avatars were not there.

"OK," said Lizzy, "I hope this works." We all teleported to a second time-, space-, and size-change travel ship called *The Beamer*. Neddy programmed a time jump for exactly 10 years and changed our size to something small to reduce time-travel duration. She hit go.

▰▰▰▰▰

We teleported back to the Mystery Museum and went to the meeting room. No one was there. Lizzy said, "I'm a little worried. Maybe our plan didn't work."

"Hey," called Neddy, looking out the window, "there's someone coming up the path. It's a woman I don't recognize."

A short time later, the woman came into the meeting room. Before we had a chance to find out who she was, we saw the *Cosmic Egg* approaching and heard it coming to a stop overhead. Then an older-looking Lizzy walked into the room.

"Hi, sister," the woman said to old Lizzy.

"Oh, wow," said young Neddy, "that's not a woman. It's me."

The first Neddy avatar had been living in the *Virtual World* for 10 years. She was now 22 years old and the tallest person in the room—even taller than me.

Lizzy reported, "Because of my slow clock after accelerating to 0.9 times the speed of light, my time travel to Proxima Centauri and back was only 4.4 years. So I am only 18 years old. Neddy, you're now four years older than me. And, wow, you got really tall."

"I so love this," said the tall Neddy, patting adult me on the top of the head.

"I wish we could have done this for real," said the young Neddy.

I took pictures of us, and we made a screenshot of our reunion. Then I added some relevent news. "They actually did a measurement to prove the paradox. They flew one clock around the Earth and compared it to an identical clock on the ground. They were different by the amount of time predicted by the _General Theory of Relativity_."

We all agreed. The _Twin Paradox_ is one of the _Five Most Unusual Things in the Universe_.

BLACK HOLES THAT EAT STARS
BY
JACKSON AND JOHARI (AS TOLD BY JACKSON)

"If I were a star," I said, "I'd want to die of spaghettification from a black hole. I mean an out-in-space star, not a movie star. Being spaghettified would be my choice for my spectacular end of life."

"Jack," interrupted Johari, "what in the world are you talking about? Nobody can understand you. What is spaghettification? You need to start at the beginning."

"OK," I agreed, "you're right. The beginning was some time in the early 1900s. A painter fell off a scaffolding on the outside of a building across the street from the patent office in Bern, Switzerland. A clerk who worked in the patent office saw the painter fall and had a thought. If the painter closed his eyes, the clerk imagined, he would not know whether he was accelerating, that is going faster and faster in freefall toward the ground, or floating in zero gravity. The clerk said it was t_he happiest thought of his life_."

"That's awful," objected Johari. "The painter would surely know the difference the second he hit the ground. You'd think this guy would have called 911. That would have been a better thought."

"OK, Jo," I answered. "The patent clerk was Albert Einstein, and the story is probably not exactly true. But Einstein really did describe his inspiration that the force of gravity and acceleration are two different parts of one single thing. He really did say that it was _the happiest thought of his life_. And that thought was the basis for his _General Theory of Relativity_.

"There is one more part to explain before we get to spaghetti," I continued. "It is Einstein's thought experiment about rockets. Even a kid can understand that part of _Relativity_. If the painter couldn't tell the difference between free falling and being in zero gravity, then the guys in the rockets can't tell if they are on the ground on Earth, feeling the force of gravity, or in a rocket ship out in space, accelerating. Think of the ship going faster and faster, that is accelerating, at the same rate as a ball that is dropped on Earth."

"Now think about shining a laser beam into the moving rocket ship," I added. "Because the ship is accelerating, the laser beam would bend, following an arc to the other side of the ship. It would follow a straight line if the rocket was standing still or moving at constant speed."

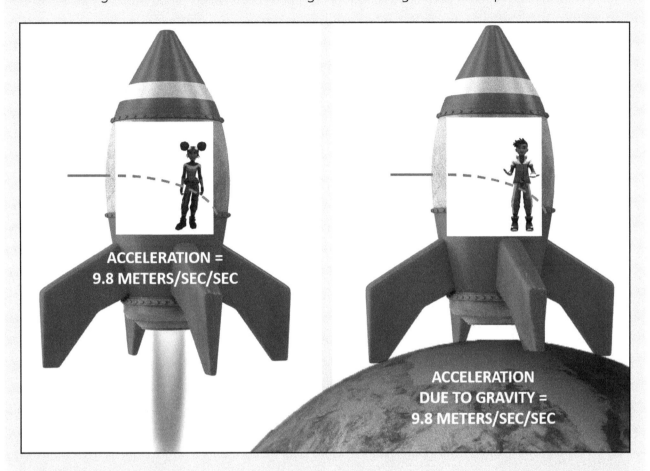

"Oh, I see," said Johari. "To the guy in the moving rocket ship, the laser beam would appear to bend. So, because Einstein predicts that the two guys should see the same thing, the beam in the rocket ship on the ground would bend too."

"Right, Jo," I answered. "And what does that mean?"

"It means that a beam of light should be bent by the force of gravity," Johari answered.

"Right again, Jo," I agreed as I gave her a pat on the head. She slapped my hand away and gave me a mean stare. "Here is the best part, Jo. Gravity bending light was actually observed in an experiment in 1919. It was during an eclipse of the sun. Just when our moon blocked the sun, the scientists could measure that light from a star was being bent by our sun, and that proved Einstein's *General Theory of Relativity*."

"So, *Boy Genius*," demanded Johari, "what in the universe does that have to do with a black hole and a star dying by spaghetti?"

"Just stick with me a little longer," I requested. "Einstein had predicted that light would be attracted by gravity. The bending of light by our sun proved it. And the bigger the object, the bigger the attraction. A star ten times larger than our sun would have ten times the force of attraction. If the mass of an object is big enough, the force of attraction could be so large that light could never escape from the object."

"I got it," said Johari. "If I throw a ball in the air, it comes back to Earth because the force of gravity pulls it back. If I shine a light upward, gravity will pull on it but not with enough force to bring it back. But if our planet were super big, it could pull the light back. Is that a black hole—an object that is so massive that no light can escape it?"

"Right, Jo," I answered. "And the force of gravity of a black hole can be so large that it can attract a star to it and gobble it up. Most galaxies have a huge black hole in their centers. Some have eaten so many stars that they have a mass that is millions or even billions of times bigger than our sun.

"So," I continued, "it's in the eating of stars where the spaghetti comes in. Sometimes as the star gets drawn to the black hole, it can get stretched and stretched. It can get shredded into long strands as it's being eaten. Astronomers have named that event spaghettification. Such an event 215 light years away was recorded by a team of astronomers at the European Southern Observatory."

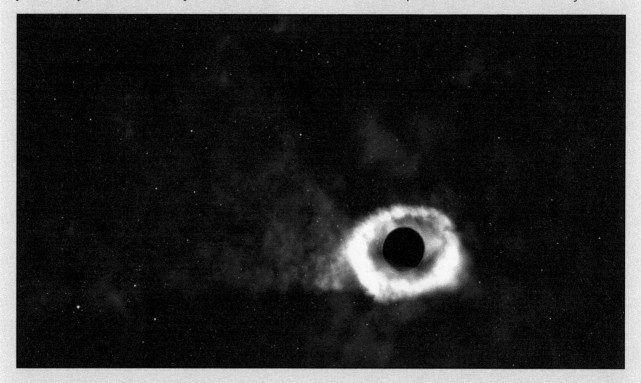

Another event was observed in January 2019 by NASA's planet-hunting Transiting Exoplanet Survey Satellite (TESS). TESS and other observatories watched a black hole rip apart a star in what was described as "*a cataclysmic phenomenon*." The event can be seen on a NASA TESS YouTube video.

Johari, the *Cosmic Explorers*, and I nominate black holes eating stars and getting bigger and bigger as number three of *The Five Most Unusual Things in the Universe*.

GRAVITATIONAL WAVES
BY
JOHARI, LIZZY, AND VC (AS TOLD BY JOHARI)

"I guess it is not surprising that so many of the unusual things in the universe were predicted by Albert Einstein," I said. "The world he predicted, which has been proven correct, is *so* different from the world of our everyday experience. That world is definitely unusual."

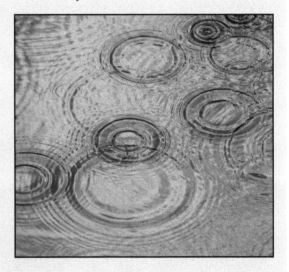

That brings us to the number-four most unusual thing in the universe according to us *Cosmic Explorers*: *Gravitational waves*.

Think about the waves caused when raindrops hit the surface of a pond. The surface waves ripple out from the point of raindrop impact in circles that expand slowly. *Gravitational waves* expand as spheres, which are 3-D circles, traveling at the speed of light away from a major cosmic disturbance. The waves are in the dimensions of space. Space actually expands and contracts—like a rippling wave on a pond!

In one project, scientists, including our team member Tom, were trying to measure *Gravitational Waves*. They were trying even though Einstein predicted that they could never be measured because they were too small.

"VC," I said, "what is the smallest thing that you know of?"

"Atoms?" she responded. "I know from the *How Big Are My Atoms* video we made during the contest last year that carbon atoms are 6 million times smaller than sand grains."

"But we know some things that are smaller," I said, "like parts of atoms: protons, neutrons, and electrons. The size of a proton is a trillion times smaller than a sand grain—1,000,000,000,000 times smaller. Let's say there is a huge cosmic event trillions of miles away. Its gravitational wave seen on Earth is expected to stretch a piece of space four kilometers long by just one-thousandth of the diameter of a proton. The scientists who Tom was working with were confident that they could make the measurement no matter what Einstein said."

The detection of gravitational waves was going to be made by LIGO, the Laser Interferometer Gravitational-Wave Observatory.

And they did it. (*Sorry, Albert!*) In 2015, they measured the *Gravitational Waves* produced by two black holes merging. The gravitational wave had been traveling at the speed of light for 1.3 billion years to reach Earth. In 2017, they detected two neutron stars merging. The event was much closer, so it only took 130 million years for the wave to arrive. What they saw on the detector from these explosive events was a tiny chirp that lasted about a minute.

"Hey," said Johari, "let's go in the *Cosmic Egg* to see the neutron star collision. It's only 130 million light years away. That's just around the corner with our *Hyper-Speed Booster*."

"I'm in," said VC and Lizzy at the same time.

We called Tom and got the location of the neutron star merger event. Then we logged into the *Virtual World*, went to the *Mystery Museum*, and teleported to the *Cosmic Egg*. VC was our *Navigator*. We time-traveled back 130 million years. Then she entered the coordinates that Tom gave us, selected the *Hyper-Speed Booster*, and off we went.

"There they are," said Lizzy. "Two tiny little stars circling each other."

We watched as the two neutron stars circled, getting closer with each rotation. Then they crashed into each other with a huge explosion. Instantly, our ship started shaking. Then the space stretching and contracting happened for about a minute. First, we were tall and thin and then short and fat. We were experiencing *Gravitational Waves* up close and personal.

"In 130 million years," observed Johari, "those waves will reach Earth and be detected by LIGO."

"Way cool," added Lizzy. "Let's head home."

DARK MATTER THAT MAY HAVE KILLED THE DINOSAURS

BY JACKSON AND RICHIE (AS TOLD BY JACKSON)

Our story starts even earlier than the Einstein stories. *Ours* starts 65 million years ago.

"Richie," I said, "what happened 65 million years ago?"

"That's easy," answered Richie. "That's when the land dinosaurs died. Now I have a question for *you*. What does a triceratops sit on? . . . Its tricera bottoms."

"Ugh, Richie, you gotta stop with the jokes," I said. "They are getting worse and worse. OK, now tell me this. How did they all die at the same time?"

"Oh, I know all about that," Richie responded. "It was a giant asteroid that killed them. It hit Earth with such force that pieces of the Earth and asteroid flew out of the atmosphere. Some stuff even went all the way to the moon. And when all that stuff started falling back and hitting the atmosphere, it created so much heat that the air got as hot as a pizza oven, and that killed all the land dinosaurs."

"Great, Richie," I continued. "Now what did that have to do with *Dark Matter*?"

"Huh?" said Richie. "I have no idea. What?"

"Well, that is our story," I responded. "Or, more exactly, it is a story told by Professor Lisa Randall of Harvard University.

"Professor Randall put the story in a book," I said. "It's called _Dark Matter and the Dinosaurs_. She proposed that *Dark Matter* could have had something to do with killing off the dinosaurs. Her idea goes like this. When scientists look at the fossil records, there appears to be evidence that a major species extinction occurs about every 33 million years. 'So,' she asks, 'is there some event that occurs every 33 million years to explain that?' Yes, there is such an event. Our solar system is in an orbit that circles the Milky Way galaxy. It takes 240 million Earth years to complete one galactic year. As it circles, our solar system oscillates up and down through the plane of the Milky Way. It passes through the plane every 33 million years.

"Grandpa made this diagram to illustrate the solar system going up and down through the Milky Way. Think of the Milky Way as a pancake, and we are looking at the edge.

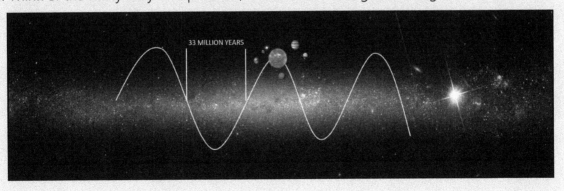

33 MILLION YEARS

"Professor Randall's idea," I continued, "is that the passage through the pancake with its higher gravitational field might knock comets and asteroids out of their normal orbits around the sun, and some of these unhinged bodies might hit Planet Earth. But calculations of this effect suggest that gravity from normal matter is not sufficient to dislodge these objects from their orbit. So Professor Randall proposes that there is some extra gravity exerted by a disk of *Dark Matter* that lies within the visible Milky Way pancake. The combined gravity from the normal matter pancake and the *Dark Matter* disk might be enough to do the job."

"What is this *Dark Matter* stuff Professor Randall is talking about?" asked Richie.

"*Dark Matter* is one of the big puzzles in physics," I answered. "*Dark Matter* is what I call a fudge factor. Scientists put it into their theories when the known physics doesn't work. So why do we need *Dark Matter*? Where does our physics not work? The answer is the structure of the universe. Normal physics says it shouldn't look like it does.

"Take a galaxy like our Milky Way," I continued. "It is rotating like pizza dough when the pizza guy throws it in the air. It gets bigger because of a force that wants to push the dough away from the center. You feel that force when you stand at the edge of a playground merry-go-round. If you don't hold on when it is spinning, you fall off. Well, gravity is holding onto the stars at the edge of the Milky Way disk as it rotates. Gravity is also holding galaxy clusters together. But gravity from the visible matter isn't enough to do the job. Our Milky Way would fly apart if the only gravity was from visible matter. So here comes the fudge factor. Let's assume there is enough extra stuff to do the job of keeping the stars from flying off the galaxies and the galaxy clusters from flying apart. But we can't see it, so the name of the stuff is *Dark Matter*. Calculations show that *Dark Matter* makes up more than 85 percent of the total matter in the universe. So the stuff that we *can* see is only 15 percent."

"That's a crazy story, Jack," said Richie. "What about this extinction happening every 33 million years? Are we due for one now? That is way scary."

"Could happen, Richie," I responded. "But we would probably see a big asteroid heading for us. So maybe we could fire up a rocket and knock it off course. Let's hope so."

We submitted the five stories. We were all pretty happy we had kept our screen times to a minimum. For *Planet Earth,* we used 15 minutes to get pictures of North America, New York City at night, and the California freeway interchange. The *Twin Paradox* took us 30 minutes. For *Black Holes That Eat Stars,* the total time was 25 minutes. *Gravitational Waves* took 15 minutes, and *Dark Matter That May Have Killed the Dinosaurs* took 10 minutes.

The total screen time for *The Five Most Unusual Things In The Universe* was 1 hour and 35 minutes.

19

FINDING THE SOURCES OF STARDUST

(AS TOLD BY RICHIE)

I am having lots of fun being on the team, and things at home are OK except for being cooped up with Leo. Luckily we haven't been fighting too much. I feel like my idea for the *Planet Colorado Space Station* will hold me for a while as far as team contributions go, but I know I still gotta improve my jokes. I've started thinking about some good ones for our next space exploration. What does a star get when it loses a contest? . . . A constellation prize! What is a light year? . . . It's the same as a regular year but with fewer calories! I know they'll like that one.

For the next part of the contest, we have to find the sources of stardust. Neddy told me all about it. She learned about stardust in last year's contest. It's atoms. They were made by stars billions of years ago and ended up inside basically everything. The stardust in my body includes carbon, oxygen, and nitrogen. Stardust is also all the heavier atoms on Earth like silver, gold, and the biggest atom, uranium. We have hydrogen in our bodies too, but hydrogen, according to Neddy, isn't stardust. Hydrogen was made during the *Big Bang* that started the universe.

Right now, our job is to find out where and when the stardust was created.

We are gonna have a *Room* meeting at noon today to plan our next mission. I logged into the meeting, and by five minutes after noon, everyone was there.

"Hey guys," called Lizzy, "take a look at the new leaderboard. We are still the leader. We actually increased our lead based on screen time used for the *Unusual Things*. But they haven't scored the bonus time for our stories yet, So we don't know where we really stand."

Time & Space Inc.

BEST INVENTION: THE COSMIC KIDS

Cosmic Explorers

THE LEADERBOARD FOR JULY 22

TEAM	% OF RACE COMPLETED	SCREEN TIME HRS USED	BONUS TIME AWARDS (HRS)
COSMIC EXPLORERS	20%	5.08	-1.0
EINSTEIN'S GIRLS	20%	7.5	-0.5
JAPAN JOURNEYERS	20%	7.7	-0.5
THE SMASH	20%	8	-0.5
AUSSIE ASTRONAUTS	20%	8	-0.5
TIME TRAVELERS	20%	8	-0.5
SPACE PIONEERS	20%	8	0
ENGLISH EXPLORERS	20%	8.5	-0.5
THE WOW	20%	8.7	0
SPANISH SPRINTERS	20%	9	0

CONTEST NEWS: The Cosmic Explorers still hold the lead in screen time. The bonus hours for *The Five Most Unusual Things In The Universe* submissions have not yet been awarded.

"Hey, everyone," said Helen, "this part of the contest about stardust is really wonderful for me. I have a quote from my favorite astronomer hanging on my office wall because I love it so much. Carl Sagan said, `*The nitrogen in our DNA, the calcium in our teeth, the iron in our blood, the carbon in our apple pies were made in the interiors of collapsing stars. We are made of starstuff.*'"

"What a great quote," agreed Johari. "I love it too. And guess what? I composed a Stardust Song, and me and some friends made a <u>Stardust Song Video</u>. I'll play it when we start the trip. I emailed the lyrics to everyone so you can sing along."

Stardust Song
Our time trip started way back in time,
four and a half billion years,
when meteors crashed, and things were hot,
and Planet Earth appears.
Formed with stardust, the building blocks,
reused throughout history.
We spin through time, our mission to solve,
the Stardust Mystery.
Stardust, we are made of stardust.
Stardust, we're all made of stardust.

"Very cool, Johari," said Tom. "Can't wait to hear it! On another note, I found a great chart on our stardust origins that should be helpful for us to plan the mission. It's a periodic table of the elements that shows the origin of each element. The chart tells you what you have to look for to find the sources of stardust."

The Origin of the Solar System Elements

1 H	big bang fusion		cosmic ray fission													2 He
3 Li	4 Be	merging neutron stars?		exploding massive stars				5 B	6 C	7 N	8 O	9 F	10 Ne
11 Na	12 Mg	dying low mass stars		exploding white dwarfs				13 Al	14 Si	15 P	16 S	17 Cl	18 Ar

19 K	20 Ca	21 Sc	22 Ti	23 V	24 Cr	25 Mn	26 Fe	27 Co	28 Ni	29 Cu	30 Zn	31 Ga	32 Ge	33 As	34 Se	35 Br	36 Kr
37 Rb	38 Sr	39 Y	40 Zr	41 Nb	42 Mo	43 Tc	44 Ru	45 Rh	46 Pd	47 Ag	48 Cd	49 In	50 Sn	51 Sb	52 Te	53 I	54 Xe
55 Cs	56 Ba		72 Hf	73 Ta	74 W	75 Re	76 Os	77 Ir	78 Pt	79 Au	80 Hg	81 Tl	82 Pb	83 Bi	84 Po	85 At	86 Rn
87 Fr	88 Ra

| 57 La | 58 Ce | 59 Pr | 60 Nd | 61 Pm | 62 Sm | 63 Eu | 64 Gd | 65 Tb | 66 Dy | 67 Ho | 68 Er | 69 Tm | 70 Yb | 71 Lu |
| 89 Ac | 90 Th | 91 Pa | 92 U | 93 Np | 94 Pu | Very radioactive isotopes; nothing left from stars |

Graphic created by Jennifer Johnson
http://www.astronomy.ohio-state.edu/~jaj/nucleo/

Astronomical Image Credits:
ESA/NASA/AASNova

We discussed the mission. Jackson prepared a space-and-time map to outline our trip, and he summarized the plan. "Task **One**, we go back to just after the *Big Bang* to check that our hydrogen has been created. Task **Two**, we go forward in time and look for the formation of high-mass stars in the newly formed Milky Way galaxy. We look near to where the solar system would eventually form."

I drew a red line that indicated the place in the Milky Way where the solar system was now.

Jackson continued. "We track the star to its death in a supernova and check the elements formed. We should see the lighter atoms. Task **Three**, we go forward in time to just before Planet Earth formed. We look for star pairs that might lead to neutron star pair collisions forming heavy elements, or we look in the same time and place for low-mass star supernovas that produced heavy elements."

Neddy asked, "Don't we already know where to find a neutron star pair collision from the LIGO event in 2017?"

"Yes, we do," answered Lizzy. "But that is way too recent to have added any atoms to Earth. The gravitational waves going at the speed of light just got here in 2017. No atoms would be here yet."

We had our plan to find the source of light atoms and two sources of heavy atoms. We ended the *Room* meeting, and all the kids logged on to the *Virtual World* and teleported to the *Cosmic Egg*.

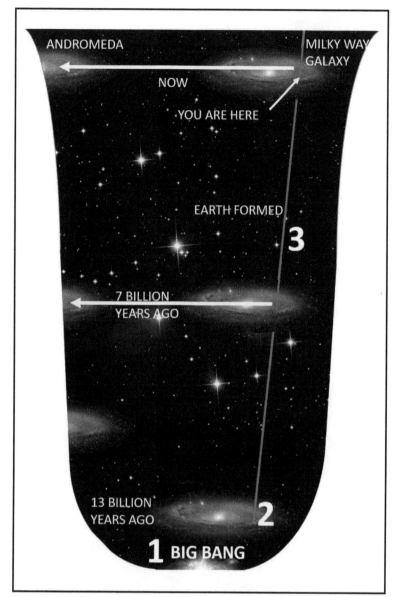

Neddy, in the role of *Navigator*, immediately reduced our ship's size by a factor of 100 so that we would save on screen time during travel. We traveled back to 200 million years after the *Big Bang* to when stars were just starting to form. The trip took just 136 seconds.

I got to be the *Scientist* for the mission.

"Richie," Jackson requested, "please do an elemental analysis of the universe."

"I'm on it," I replied. "I'm reading 75% hydrogen, 25% helium, and a tiny bit of lithium."

"OK," said Jackson, "our hydrogen and helium atoms were formed in the *Big Bang*. That's step **One**. Now let's pick a star that is forming and follow its life cycle. Lizzy, would you please advance time by 1 million years per second."

We watched as the clouds of gas started to clump and accumulate mass. Finally, the mass got large enough to become a star, and the <u>fusion reaction</u> of hydrogen atoms combining to form helium ignited. The star started to shine brightly. Soon, other stars joined it in the space around us.

"I measured the mass of these stars," said Jackson. "They are between 10 and 30 times bigger than our sun. They are definitely high-mass stars."

After about 100 seconds, which was 100 million years, our star started to dim and then started to collapse, and that's when it happened. The star went supernova! It exploded in a blinding flash of fire and gases. It was pretty much the raddest thing I've ever seen.

"Wow," said Neddy, "look at that huge explosion! That's definitely a supernova. Cool! That's step **Two**."

"Richie," suggested Jackson, "do the chemical analysis and put it on the big computer screen."

Sure enough, we saw what we were looking for. "There's our first stardust," yelled Jackson. "See them? Carbon, oxygen, and nitrogen—all the lighter atoms in our bodies."

"And more too," I added. "We got atoms all the way up to Zr from that star. That's zirconium," I added, winking at Neddy. I loved it when I surprised her by knowing stuff.

"OK, let's go ahead in time to step **Three**," said Neddy. She always had to be bossy.

We reduced our size to save screen time during time travel and advanced to 7 billion years ago. We zoomed over *Planet Colorado* to make sure it was OK. It was rad. It had an ocean and clouds and a blue atmosphere. It was almost as pretty as Planet Earth, if I do say so myself. We continued advancing time to 6 billion years ago, where we stopped to look for a cosmic event that could have produced even more stardust. Jackson was our expert for this part of our search because he and Helen had already discussed in detail what we needed to do.

"We need to look for star pairs that are connected by gravity and circling one another," instructed Jackson. "They need to be about six times larger than our sun."

"Jack," objected Lizzy, "I thought we were looking for neutron star pairs."

"We are," answered Jackson. "But neutron star pairs are way too small by themselves for us to find. They are only the size of, like, New York City. We would never see them."

"But New York City is huge," VC pointed out.

"Yeah, but we need to look for things bigger than our *sun*, you know," Jackson explained. "We're looking for the stars that *created* the neutron star pairs in order to find the neutron star pairs themselves."

I had to hand it to the guy. It made sense. He must be smart 'cause he is already in college.

So we all got to work looking for a pair of giant stars that were dancing with each other. While we looked,

Johari sang the stardust song. Me and Neddy joined her. I felt worried that we were chewing up screen time with our search, but I didn't say anything.

After half an hour, Lizzy spotted a likely star pair. Jackson used our telescope and thought it looked promising, so we started heading toward them.

"Oh, wow," yelled Lizzy, "did you guys see that? A pretty big asteroid just went whizzing over the top of the ship."

"Oh, man," VC added, "there is another one. We could be going through an asteroid belt. If one of them hits us, it is game over. It'll destroy our ship, and we will be out of the contest."

"Richie," yelled Jackson, "launch the drone so we can get a better view of what is coming at us. It will help us take evasive action to avoid getting hit."

With the view from the drone, we could see a monster asteroid just about to hit the back of the ship. Jackson ran to the controls and did a size change to make us 100 times smaller. The asteroid whizzed past in back of our small ship.

"Wow, that was close," screamed Lizzy. "Quick thinking, Jack."

Jackson continued at the ship's navigation station to pilot us out of the asteroid belt, dodging and speeding to avoid collisions. Lizzy took over the *Guardian* role and used her *time-freeze* tool to stop some of the asteroids. We arrived at our twin stars without any more trouble.

"Lizzy," called Jackson, "please advance our time."

At our small size, it only took 10 seconds to advance a billion years. Then we saw both stars dim and start to shrink. Then they exploaded into simultaneous supernovas. What was left after the explosions were two tiny stars that were circling each other. They were the neutron stars we were looking for.

"Wow," said Neddy, "those were huge explosions. Let's see if we got any stardust."

I did a chemical analysis of the exploded gas from the star supernovas for task **Three**. "We did," I responded, checking my readouts. "The whole periodic table is now filled in. Heavy atoms were produced in the star supernovas."

"Hey, team," reported Jackson, "that little star is only about 20 kilometers in diameter. New York City is about 25 kilometers. But that star has a *mass* equal to our sun. The density of that thing is like the density of an <u>atom's nucleus.</u>"

"It's like me," I said, making a muscle with my fist in the air. "I'm small but dense!"

"You got the dense part right." My supposed friend Neddy chuckled.

A few good eyerolls later, we were still moving forward in time. Those two neutron stars continued circling but kept getting closer and closer to each other. Lizzy took a picture of one of them. Then they suddenly merged and exploded.

"Wow," said Neddy again, "that was another huge explosion. Let's see if we got some more stardust."

"We did," I responded, checking my readouts. "Heavy atoms were produced in both the star supernovas and the merging neutron stars."

"Good job, everyone," said Jackson. "I think that's it. We can head for home."

"I think we did well," reported Neddy, who was checking her computer. "That mission took us just an hour and a quarter of screen time."

"Now let's get ready for the next mission," added VC. "I am in charge of that one."

20

THE UNIVERSE SEVEN BILLION YEARS AGO TO NOW

[AS TOLD BY VC]

I wasn't sure why the team put me in charge of this mission, but I would try to do my best. Life at home during the pandemic was OK since we created the family bubble, and I got to see my cousins and grandparents. It let me get out of the house and away from my little brother, Griffin. Griffy was really smart, but he can definitely drive a girl nuts with his constant questions. I went to visit my cousins when the urge to kill him got too great, so that was good.

I read through the rules for our next mission to prepare for my leadership role. There was a whole list of things that we needed to find and photograph. They could all be found somewhere between 7 billion years ago and today. So, you know, easy peasy. Except not at all! Well, OK, some of the things on the list sounded like they might be pretty easy to find, like *two black holes merging*. I knew about things like that because Papa told me about them. It was the specific event that created the first gravitational waves observed by LIGO, the Laser Interferometer Gravitational-Wave Observatory.

But some things didn't make much sense to me, like we had to find something called *the middle of the sword*. I was worried I was going to mess this whole thing up. So I was thrilled that we had a team meeting coming up to discuss the mission.

Time & Space Inc.

BEST INVENTION: THE COSMIC KIDS

Space Pioneers

THE LEADERBOARD FOR JULY 29

TEAM	% OF RACE COMPLETED	SCREEN TIME HRS USED	BONUS TIME AWARDS (HRS)
COSMIC EXPLORERS	40%	6.33	-1.0
EINSTEIN'S GIRLS	40%	8.5	-1.0
SPACE PIONEERS	40%	8.5	-1.0
JAPAN JOURNEYERS	40%	8.7	-1.0
THE SMASH	40%	8.9	-1.0
AUSSIE ASTRONAUTS	40%	9.0	-1.0
TIME TRAVELERS	40%	9.0	-0.5
ENGLISH EXPLORERS	40%	9.5	-0.5
THE WOW	40%	10.0	0
SPANISH SPRINTERS	40%	10.5	0

Everyone was there just after noon. Of course, the first thing we had to talk about was the *leaderboard*. We were still in first place overall, but our lead had been cut from about 3 hours to a little over 2 hours. And the big news was that Milo's team had won the overall competition for *The Five Most Unusual Things in the Universe*.

"Look," I said, "Svetlana's team just pasted Milo's dumb picture into last year's team photo."

I thought we were robbed because our choices were so good. They had four of the same ones, including the *Twin Paradox* because, obviously, their team had two sets of twins. But instead of gravitational waves, they had <u>quasars</u>. I guess the judges liked that better. So that moved them up to a tie for second place. The one thing we all agreed upon was that we couldn't let Milo beat us.

"Hey, guys," observed Johari, "look at all the small-time additions for the *Stardust Mission*. Everyone must have figured out that traveling with their ships at a small size means it takes less time. We no longer have our advantage. The secret is out."

We all sort of sighed sadly at that, but it had probably been too good to be true. We moved on to a discussion of the things on the list that we had to find.

"Does anyone have any idea what *the middle of the sword* could be?" I asked.

Helen, whom I was starting to really love and wanted to be like when I grew up, came up with the answer. "I'll bet that refers to the sword in the constellation Orion." She shared a picture of Orion she had on her computer. "There is a really beautiful star cluster in the middle, and there are supernovas coming from there too. It's called the Great Orion Nebula."

"How about *950 times bigger than the sun*?" asked Lizzy. "What's that?"

After searching on her computer, Helen once again had a great answer. "I think they want us to find *Betelgeuse*. Betelgeuse is one of the largest stars in the Milky Way. It's part of the Orion constellation too. It's the left shoulder."

Then we had this talk about how it was spelled because Richie thought it was Beetlejuice, like a movie he loves, which I think Papa loves too. And then Lizzy was like, "No, it's like the juice of a beetle, so two words."

Then Neddy shut us up by stating that it was "Betelgeuse," which, in Arabic, meant *"the hand of Orion"* or *"the armpit of Orion."* She spelled it for us.

After we finished discussing what each list item was, Jackson put them in the order that we would look for them. He added the stop location in time and space to his map. We were ready to go. The meeting took 3 hours, so we decided to get a fresh start at 11:00 a.m. the next day.

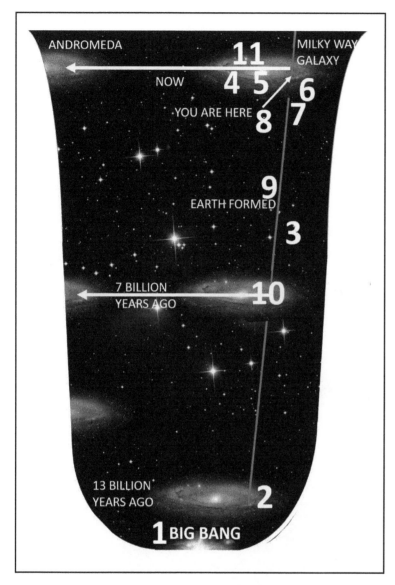

MISSION STOPS

Stop Four: Center of the sword (1,350 years ago)

Stop Five: 950 times larger than the sun (1,350 years ago)

Stop Six: Event that saved the dinosaurs (201 million years ago)

Stop Seven: Pangea (300 million years ago)

Stop Eight: Merging black holes (1.3 billion years ago)

Stop Nine: Asteroid that made the moon (4.4 billion years ago)

Stop Ten: Find two other space stations (7 billion years ago)

Stop Eleven: Most artistic photo

▰ ▰ ▰ ▰ ▰

That night, I took Griffy out in the backyard to show him the constellation Orion. That was going to be the first part of our mission for the next day. Orion was beautifully visible in the sky.

"There's Orion, Griffy," I explained as I pointed to Orion's stars. "See if you can see a person in those stars. The bright star on the top is his head. Then there are two stars for his shoulders. The three stars on a slanted line in the center is his belt, and his sword hangs down from his belt. The two bottom stars are his feet."

"I see it," said Griffin. "He's cool."

"Orion is part of a lot of different legends," I continued. "In one, he is a hunter. He is tall and handsome, and he's the son of the sea god, Poseidon. In another, he fights a bull, also outlined in stars. Tomorrow we are going to visit two places in the Orion constellation. It's eight thousand trillion miles away. Its starlight takes 1,350 years to get here. First, we'll visit the center star on his sword. It is actually a star factory where new stars are being born with gas collected by gravity. It is called the Great Orion Nebula. Then we'll visit his left shoulder, a star called *Betelgeuse*. It is one of the largest stars in the Milky Way. It is 950 times heavier than our star, the sun."

"Beetle Juice," he said, laughing about the name too. "That is a funny name. It's gotta be made from squished beetles, right?"

"Yeah," I agreed as I led him back to the house for bedtime, "it's gotta be made from squished beetles."

■ ■ ■ ■ ■

The next day, at ten after eleven in the morning, we were logged on to the *Virtual World*. We teleported to the *Cosmic Egg* and were on our way to Orion for stops **Four** and **Five**. We were going back 1,350 years to see Orion at the time it released the light that we see on Earth today. Stop **Four** was the Great Orion Nebula. It was beautiful. We took a photo that we could submit for the most beautiful part of our mission.

"All those swirling colors make it look like an abstract painting," Johari observed.

"The swirling colors come from all the space gases," said Jackson. "Those gases are getting concentrated by gravity to form new stars. That's our universe growing and evolving."

"Cool," I said. "OK, guys, time to move on to stop **Five**."

Neddy piloted the *Cosmic Egg* to Orion's left shoulder to see *Betelgeuse*, the star with a mass of 950 suns.

"That is definitely the biggest star I have ever seen," declared Lizzy. "It's awesome."

"*Awesome?*" asked Neddy. "That's what Milo would say. You would say *cool*."

"I hate to say it," confessed Lizzy, "but I do kinda miss him. He must be creeping into my brain."

I kind of agreed, even though I didn't admit it. Milo was a traitor, plain and simple.

We took some photos of *Betelgeuse* and moved to stop **Six**, Planet Earth 201 million years ago. We were looking for an event that saved the dinosaurs.

"I did the research on that," said Neddy. "It's the *Triassic Jurassic Extinction Event* we are looking for—that started the Jurassic period, when the dinosaurs ruled. Most scientists believe that huge volcanic eruptions released high amounts of carbon dioxide to cause global warming. The higher temperatures weren't good for a lot of the other large land animals that competed with the dinosaurs. They needed cooler climates, so the dinosaurs took over. We need to find the volcanos."

We started circling the planet while we went slowly back in time from 200 million years ago.

"Look at that," observed Lizzy, "the continents have all moved. North and South America are almost touching Africa."

Close to 201 million years ago, we saw volcanos erupting. They were off the west coast of Africa, and there were lots of them. The eruptions continued as we went back in time for about 600 thousand years. We took more photos and then started moving further back in time to stop **Seven**.

By 300 million years ago, the seven continents were all squashed together into one big continent called Pangaea. We took some stop **Seven** photos.

"I know all about stop **Eight**," I announced. "Papa told me all about it. It is the merger of two black holes that was the first detected gravitational wave by LIGO. It was detected on September 9, 2015. The gravitational wave came from over 1.3 billion years ago, and we know the location it came from."

So off we went. We changed size to save on time-travel screen time. We used our *Hyper-Speed Booster* for space travel.

To find the exact location, we spent some of our gold to order the <u>Multi-Messenger Astronomy</u> <u>system</u>. It included a portable LIGO detector. Jackson installed the system and turned it on. Within a few minutes of searching, he got a gravitational wave signal. We moved in a direction that made the signal stronger.

"Wow," said Neddy, "there they are. They are dancing around each other. I'll move us forward in time to see the merger."

The two black holes merged, and the gravitational wave hit us, shaking the ship.

"Hey," yelled Johari, "we have a problem. We are moving closer to the new, big black hole. Neddy, you'd better move us away."

"It's not working," called Neddy. "I'm using full power, but we are still being pulled toward the black hole. We're getting closer and closer."

"This isn't good," yelled Lizzy. "If we get sucked into the black hole, we destroy the *Cosmic Egg*, and we are out of the competition. We need to do something."

"Lizzy, try changing our size," yelled Jackson.

"That's not working," called Neddy, who spent 15 minutes piloting the ship with different settings. "When we are smaller, there is less pull, but we go slower. When we're bigger, we can go faster, but there is more pull from the black hole. We are still getting closer to doom."

"OK, I have an idea," proposed Jackson. "Instead of trying to go directly away from the black hole, try to circle it. Maybe we can spiral out away from it."

Ten minutes later, Neddy reported, "No, not working, Jack. Think, guys, think. We are getting closer and closer. This could be very bad."

"How about using the *Hyper-Speed Booster*?" suggested Johari.

Lizzy started working at the controls to get the *Hyper-Speed Booster* engaged. "I can't get it to turn on," she screamed. "I think we need to be back at normal size."

"I got that," said Neddy, who quickly changed our size setting.

"OK, I got it engaged," reported Lizzy. "But it is not doing anything except shaking the ship. It doesn't seem to work against the huge pull of the black hole's gravity."

Then I got the idea that saved us. "Lizzy, just back up in time to before the merger. Then we should be able to move away."

Lizzy smiled hugely as she changed where we were in time. Two minutes later, we were in the clear. My idea had worked! We all cheered and did high fives and fist bumps.

With the emergency over, we time-traveled back to the merged black hole with a lot of distance between us for safety. This time I took photographs to record the whole merging sequence for our report. When we started getting drawn into the black hole, we knew what to do.

The only problem? Our near-disaster had taken us a whole extra 45 minutes of screen time.

For stop **Nine**, we used the *Hyper-Speed Booster* to travel back to Earth and then time-traveled to 4.4 billion years ago to witness the formation of our moon. We moved to a time when Earth had no moon and then went forward in time. We watched it happen.

We watched a giant asteroid smack into Planet Earth. Earth shook and deformed, and then a large piece flew off into orbit.

"That's our moon," declared Neddy. Doing a perfect imitation of her sister channeling Milo, she said, "Awesome."

"It's a good thing that we weren't around when this happened," observed Jackson. "No life on Earth would have survived the impact."

We went on to stop **Ten**, finding two space stations from other teams 7 billion years ago as part of our scavenger hunt. That was easy. No one else used a planet for a space station, so all the stations were right in the location where Earth had later formed. That was on Jackson's map as the red line. We found the space station of Milo's team, which cloned part of their time/spaceship, right away. We also found a bunch of space stations that used parts of the *International Space Station*.

For stop **Eleven**, we agreed that the most beautiful thing we found was the *Great Orion Nebula* that we had photographed at stop **Four**. The volcanos from stop **Six** came in second.

It was time to end the mission. We traveled to our *Planet Colorado Space Station* and teleported to the surface, where we entered the headquarters building. That is where we were supposed to log off. But when we were inside, something strange was going on.

"What are all those noises coming from outside?" asked Neddy.

"Yeah, I heard it too," I agreed. "But the instructions say to log off. We can look into it when we start the next mission."

We had used a total of two hours of screen time for this mission by the time we logged off.

21

THE UNIVERSE BEFORE SEVEN BILLION YEARS AGO

(AS TOLD BY JOHARI)

The singing lessons had been going great. I really loved singing, and I did it all around the house. It was kinda driving Jackson batty. So much the better. Dad and I were still running on the beach. Except for the *Virtual World* missions, that was the best part of the day. Turns out pandemics are way boring.

Today's *Cosmic Explorer* team meeting is at 11:00 a.m. Eastern time. It is totally unfair. The East Coast kids can sleep till eleven in the morning, and I have to get up at 8:00 a.m. That's like the middle of the night!

"Good morning," I said to the team when I logged on to our *Room* call. "Did everyone see the latest leaderboard?"

"Oh, yeah, I saw it," griped Lizzy. "Milo's team won the top bonus hours award for *Finding the Sources of Stardust*. Top prize again—oh man!"

"And they are in second place," observed Neddy. "We are now leading by only 0.17 hours when you figure in the bonus hours. And our trouble with the black hole on the last mission is going to hurt our standing even more," she groaned.

"OK, let's make sure we do a good job on this mission," I commanded. "The first part of the mission is to make a video at our space station. We need to do a tour of the station, and each of the team members needs to tell a little about themselves. Lizzy, can you plan the video?

Time & Space Inc.

BEST INVENTION: THE COSMIC KIDS

Space Pioneers

THE LEADERBOARD FOR AUGUST 5

TEAM	% OF RACE COMPLETED	SCREEN TIME HRS USED	BONUS TIME AWARDS (HRS)
COSMIC EXPLORERS	60%	8.33	-1.0
SPACE PIONEERS	60%	9.5	-2.0
EINSTEIN'S GIRLS	60%	10.5	-1.5
JAPAN JOURNEYERS	60%	10.9	-1.5
TIME TRAVELERS	60%	10.0	-0.5
THE SMASH	60%	11.5	-1.5
AUSSIE ASTRONAUTS	60%	10.5	-1.0
ENGLISH EXPLORERS	60%	11.0	-0.5
THE WOW	60%	12.0	-.5
SPANISH SPRINTERS	60%	13.5	0

CONTEST NEWS: The Space Pioneers win the top award for the best entries for *Finding the Sources of Stardust*. The Cosmic Explorers still lead by a narrow margin.

"Then," I continued, "just like our last mission, we have a list of cosmic objects to find and photograph. Jack, can you take charge of the list? Please put them in order on your map."

We discussed the items on the list. Jackson put them on the map, and we were ready to go.

We'll start at 11:00 a.m. tomorrow.

█ █ █ █ █

The following morning, we all printed copies of Jackson's map and the list of mission stops that he had emailed.

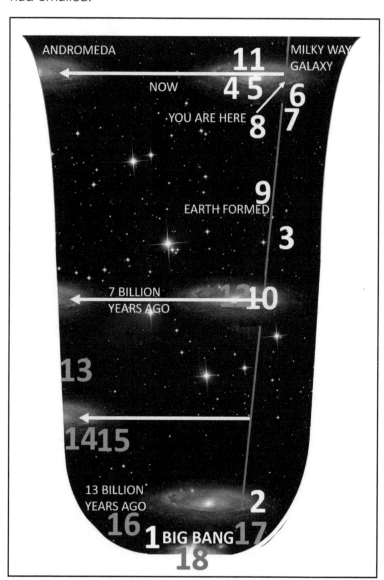

MISSION STOPS

Stop Twelve: *Planet Colorado Space Station* video (7 billion years ago)

Stop Thirteen: The most distant star (9 billion years ago)

Stop Fourteen: A mass of 66 billion suns (10.4 billion years ago)

Stop Fifteen: The oldest supernova (10.5 billion years ago)

Stop Sixteen: The most distant object (13.4 billion years ago)

Stop Seventeen: The oldest star is born (13.6 billion years ago)

Stop Eighteen: It has colors and charm and comes in 6 flavors (13.8 billion years ago)

We started the mission. We logged on to the *Virtual World* and were spawned into the *Planet Colorado Space Station* headquarters building, where we had finished the previous mission.

Richie started us off with one of his dumb jokes: "Why don't stars go to college? . . . Because they already have a million degrees."

Everyone groaned.

Since we were on *Planet Colorado,* I thought it would be appropriate to start us off with my rendition of John Denver's "Rocky Mountain High."

"I've seen it rainin' fire in the sky." I sang softly first and finished loudly with *"Rocky mountain high (Colorado)."*

"OK, team," my brother interrupted, "we are wasting screen time. We need to get started with stop **Twelve.** That means doing interviews about ourselves and giving a tour of our space station. As we tour, we need to explain the station's parts and how we built it. Why don't you girls do the tour outside of the headquarters? Richie and I will do the tour inside."

"I'm a little worried about those noises that I heard outside when we finished the last mission," admitted Neddy. "But I don't hear them anymore, so I guess I am OK with going outside."

"Why?" Richie asked, blanching a little. "What do you think it was?"

"I don't know," Neddy replied. "I guess it could be just about anything. Remember, this is a strange planet. We don't know what's out there."

So, on that scary note, out we went and started our tour. We were screen capturing our scenes to make the required video. I explained how we found the planet, and Lizzy explained the green slime. Neddy explained how we got water from comets and how we planted seeds.

We were walking ahead of Neddy, who stopped to look at something. "Hey guys," she called, "look across the river at the . . ."

But before she could finish, we knew exactly what it was, and we were already running. An over-sized grasshopper had charged us from the woods. The three of us passed Neddy, who was still staring across the river.

"Neddy," screamed Lizzy, "stop staring into space and run for your life! We gotta get back to head-quarters before we get eaten by bugs."

We made it to headquarters with the green monster hot on our heels. We went inside and slammed the door. I was bent over trying to catch my breath like the other kids. Jackson and Richie came over and looked out the windows. The room darkened as the headquarters became surrounded by a bunch of humongous insects all sticking to the windows.

"They smell our fear," whispered Richie. "Where did they come from?"

"They must have evolved out of something in the seeds or the green slime that we brought," offered VC.

"It may be the low gravity and the high concentration of oxygen in the atmosphere that let them get so big," suggested Jackson.

"They also don't have any predators," Neddy added.

The giant insects surrounding us were increasing in number. Some were even climbing on the roof of the headquarters. They were poking at the glass, trying to break in. My guess is that they were thinking of a tasty meal.

"I hear glass breaking," screamed Neddy. "It's time to get outta here."

Everyone agreed, and we all teleported to the *Cosmic Egg*, which was hovering overhead.

We looked back down on what we had created. We were in a state of shock. All of *Planet Colorado* was covered in giant insects.

"Brilliant idea, Richie," I teased.

"Come on, you guys," said Neddy. "This was not Richie's fault. And remember, the idea did get us the $25,000 first prize."

"You're right, Neddy," agreed Jackson. "How do we fix this?"

"You guys," said Lizzy, who looked white as a sheet, probably because she'd been chased by a giant insect during the previous competition, and she was having a little bit of PTSD, "we are *not* going to be defeated by a bunch of bugs."

"What should we do?" asked Richie.

"Let's go back in time," Lizzy responded, "and plant citronella grass, chrysanthemums, and chamomile all around the station. That's what Grandma plants in her garden as natural bug repellents."

"Great idea," said Neddy.

"We have to be quick," Jack reminded us. "Time is everything."

Neddy found that we could buy the plants and have them shipped to us. It took half of our gold *currency* but only five precious minutes. Then, since we only had to go back in time fifteen years to get a lush growth from our perennial plants, that was not even a whole second. It took ten minutes to scatter all of the seeds while piloting the *Cosmic Egg* around the station. Then we went back to the original time to see how we did. Sure enough, the plants had grown in thickly and lushly around the station. There were no bugs nearby on the ground. A few flying creatures were overhead, but none flew down to the station. Our problem solving had worked!

We high fived.

"Now let's go down to headquarters," said Jackson, "and finish the videos. Then let's get on to stop **Thirteen** to find an object that is 66 billion times larger than our sun."

We finished the videos, returned to the *Cosmic Egg*, and reduced our size for efficient time travel. Then it was on to Stop **Thirteen**, 9 billion years ago.

Jackson advised, "We are looking for the farthest star ever seen from Earth. Helen told me what to look for and where to find it. It was seen more than halfway across the universe using NASA's Hubble Space Telescope. It is an enormous blue star nicknamed Icarus."

We had to use our *Hyper-Speed Booster* to make the long trip across the universe. We found what we were looking for and photographed it for our report.

Our next destination was 10.4 billion years ago for stop **Fourteen**. Helen said we were looking for a *quasar* called TON 618. "It shines 140 trillion times brighter than our sun. It's the *quasar's* massive black hole that is 66 billion times bigger than our sun. It's the largest known object in the universe."

"Wow," exclaimed Neddy, "we think of our sun as something huge. Imagine an object that is 66 billion times bigger. Wow!"

Shining as brightly as it does, it was not hard to find. We traveled to it and photographed it for our mission report.

A short hop in time brought us to stop **Fifteen** at 10.5 billion years ago. It was the oldest supernova that had ever been observed. We moved slowly back through time to look for a bright star-like object that would suddenly appear. It would look very bright, and then it would dim back down to normal star brightness. In 10 minutes of screen time, we found it and photographed it.

We also measured the distance between *Andromeda* and the Milky Way. It was just 75% of its value in the present time. Professor Lemaître was going to be thrilled.

Stop **Sixteen** was the most distant object ever seen. It was a galaxy 32 billion light-years away. We could see it from Earth as it existed 13.4 billion years ago. Its designation was GN-z11.

"Hey," said Jackson, "think about this. On present-day Earth, the light we see coming from GN-z11 started traveling toward us over thirteen *billion* years ago."

At 13.4 billion years ago, we space traveled farther and farther away from our Milky Way. Even with the location in the universe that Helen had given us, it took us over half an hour of screen time to find the distant galaxy.

"I think this must be it," Jackson declared when we couldn't see any galaxies farther away. "Let's get a photo for our report."

For stop **Seventeen**, we traveled back to 13.6 billion years ago. That was just 200 million years after the *Big Bang*. We were looking for the oldest star that had been seen from Earth. It had the designation HD 140283, but astronomers called it Methuselah, after the Bible figure who was said to have lived to be 969 years old. In the present time, the star was 190 light-years away, so it is in the Milky Way. Helen gave us the location, and we found a star that we thought must be it.

"For stop **Eighteen**," said Jackson, "we are looking for something that has colors and charm and comes in six flavors. Does anyone know what that is?"

"That must be me," offered Neddy. "I have lots of charm, and I wear lots of different colors."

"Brilliant," Lizzy said sarcastically.

"I know," I answered. "They are *quarks*. I guess living with Jackson is good for something."

"Yes," responded Jackson. "They are the building blocks that make protons and neutrons. To see *quarks*, we need to go all the way back to the *Big Bang* 13.8 billion years ago. We need to go to just one second after the *Big Bang*, before the *quarks* got assembled into protons and neutrons.

"Lizzy," he called, "please change the size of the *Cosmic Egg* to *quark* size so we can see them. "Quarks are really, really small. They're like 10 million billion times smaller than a sand grain."

We changed our size and traveled back in time to one second after the *Big Bang*. We could see the little tiny *quarks* flying all around outside our window. Actually, what we saw was just the *Virtual World* representation of the *quarks* to indicate their different kinds, such as up and down, and different colors. VC and Lizzy went up on the *Cosmic Egg* work deck to see them. VC even tried to capture some with the *grab* tool. That was good practice for the final mission, which was to build the first atoms starting from *quarks* and electrons. I took a screenshot for our mission report.

Scene from "Building the First Atoms in the Universe." **The STARDUST MYSTERY YouTube Channel**

The trouble at *Planet Colorado* had cost us lots of screen time. The total for this mission was three hours and fifteen minutes.

THE BIG BANG AND THE FIRST ATOMS

(AS TOLD BY JACKSON)

On our final mission we reached the first second after the *Big Bang*, when the universe was very small and very hot. It consisted of *quarks* and electrons and nothing else. With these components, we had to build the first atoms in the universe. They were hydrogen and helium. Those atoms formed automatically in the intense heat of the *Big Bang*. But in the *Virtual World*, we were going to assemble them ourselves from the quarks and electrons as a learning exercise. We were going to use an *assembly sphere* where we would put the components in the right places and then join them together with the proper forces.

We started off with a *Room* meeting to plan the mission. First, we looked at the leaderboard.

"Wow, this is kind of a disaster for us," said Johari. "The *Cosmic Explorers* dropped from being the contest leaders to third place!" We had previously held the lowest total screen time by 0.17 hours. Now we trailed Milo's team by 1.08 hours.

"Maybe we spent too much time trying to stop the bugs on *Planet Colorado*," offered Lizzy. "And we got penalized half an hour because the bugs made our space station unusable. We've gotta do really well on the next mission to catch up."

Time & Space Inc.

BEST INVENTION: THE COSMIC KIDS

Space Pioneers

THE LEADERBOARD FOR AUGUST 7

TEAM	% OF RACE COMPLETED	SCREEN TIME HRS USED	BONUS TIME AWARDS (HRS)
SPACE PIONEERS	80%	11.50	-2.0
TIME TRAVELERS	80%	11.00	-1.0
COSMIC EXPLORERS	80%	11.08	-0.5
EINSTEIN'S GIRLS	80%	12.50	-1.5
JAPAN JOURNEYERS	80%	12.50	-1.5
THE SMASH	80%	13.10	-1.5
AUSSIE ASTRONAUTS	80%	12.80	-1.0
ENGLISH EXPLORERS	80%	13.00	-0.5
THE WOW	80%	13.20	-0.5
SPANISH SPRINTERS	80%	13.50	0

CONTEST NEWS: The Space Pioneers move into first place, the Time Travelers move into second, and the Cosmic Explorers drop to third place. The Cosmic Explorers have lost ½ hour of their bonus time award due to the insect infestation of their space station.

We spent an hour planning the mission. The plan was to split into three teams and attempt the assembly of hydrogen and helium simultaneously. Then each team did a practice run of our steps.

"I bet we can do the mission in 20 minutes if we're careful and quick," I proposed.

Once we felt confident that we knew what we were doing, we logged on and ordered two additional *assembly spheres*—where we would build our atoms—and two additional sets of all the tools we needed. We paid extra for immediate delivery to the ship. This cost us all of our remaining gold currency.

We went to work. First, we needed to collect the *quarks* and electrons. VC had already practiced that in the last mission. VC, Neddy, and I went up on the work deck, which had a heat shield to protect us. Using the *grab* tools, we collected several copies of the six different *quarks*, 3 colors of up *quarks* and 3 colors of down. That filled up the inventory boxes on the flight deck. We were going to use the *quarks* to build protons and neutrons that form the nucleus or center of each atom.

"OK, Lizzy and VC," I commanded, "you guys build a neutron."

Lizzy had to get a triangle template to assemble the *quarks*. Meanwhile, VC had to collect two down *quarks* and one up *quark*, each in three different colors. We don't know what they would really look like, but in the *Virtual World* the *quarks* had different colors and arrows to represent up and down. VC needed to collect them, put them into the template, and then put everything into the assembly sphere. After that was done, Lizzy would hit the assembly with three <u>gluons</u> from her *gluon gun* tool. The three gluons fused the *quarks* into a neutron.

VC put the finished neutron into the inventory and then repeated the process to make several more copies.

Scenes from *"Building the First Atoms in the Universe."* The STARDUST MYSTERY YouTube Channel

"OK, Neddy and Richie," I ordered, "now you guys do the same process to make a proton, except for protons, you need two up *quarks* and one down *quark*. Again, you need three different colors of each."

Neddy and Richie made 4 protons in 2 minutes, while Lizzy and VC made the neutrons.

As soon as the first proton was made, Johari and I started turning them into hydrogen atoms. We put the proton in the center of our assembly sphere, shot in an electron, and zapped the pair with the electromagnetic force gun. That created the attractive force between the proton and electron. The electron started circling around the nucleus in an orbit. It was kinda like how the moon circles the Earth.

When we finished making several hydrogen atoms, Johari and I started to make heavy hydrogens. For that, we used one proton and one neutron for the nucleus. We added a single electron and the electromagnetic force. We made a bunch and added them to the inventory. Then we made tritium, which has one proton and two neutrons in the nucleus.

"OK," I said to Lizzy and VC, who had finished making neutrons, "now make helium atoms." A helium nucleus required two protons and two neutrons in the center of the assembly sphere. To make helium, they had to shoot two electrons into the sphere.

At first, the electrons bounced around wildly.

"Now Lizzy," I instructed, "add the electromagnetic force to make the electrons stick to the nucleus."

Scenes from "Building the First Atoms in the Universe." **The STARDUST MYSTERY YouTube Channel**

Lizzy did it, and it worked.

"Cool," said VC. "Now the two electrons are circling around the nucleus in orbits. It's like the two moons on that egg-shaped planet that Helen loves so much."

We did one final task for the mission. Neddy and Richie put all the hydrogen, heavy hydrogen, and tritium into the assembly sphere. Then Lizzy started cranking up the sphere's temperature.

"We are going to witness the nuclear fusion reaction that takes place on our sun to produce light and heat," I said. "It's the same reaction that actually formed the helium in the *Big Bang*."

The first thing that happened at several thousand degrees Celsius was that the electrons all detached from the nuclei. When the temperature reached 100 million degrees Celsius, each time a tritium nucleus hit a heavy hydrogen nucleus, the two fused to form a helium nucleus, and the extra neutron went flying off at a tremendous velocity. We were watching the nuclear fusion reaction take place.

We did all the experiments in just 19 minutes. We accomplished our mission.

23

THE MILLION DOLLAR GRAND PRIZE

(AS TOLD BY LIZZY)

We were all logged in to a *Room* meeting on August 17 at 11:45 a.m. EST. The leaderboard was due to be posted at noon. I screen shared the TSI contest website, and we discussed our last mission as we waited anxiously for the results to appear.

At exactly twelve o'clock, it appeared on the screen, and Jackson yelled, "Great! We made up almost 30 minutes on the building atoms mission. The *Space Pioneers* are less than 30 minutes ahead of us in total screen time."

"Cool," said VC. "There is just one final part of the contest. If we get the top bonus, we could win first place. We'll win at least second or third place if we get any one of the best picture and story bonus awards!"

"But I want to beat those guys," I screamed. But I mostly meant Milo. "We just have to. We need a genius idea for the final task. We have to pick the best picture and best story for the whole race to the *Big Bang*."

We'll find out who wins on August 30. That's when the top 10 teams are invited to the final meeting

Time & Space Inc.

BEST INVENTION: THE COSMIC KIDS

Space Pioneers

THE LEADERBOARD FOR AUGUST 17

TEAM	% OF RACE COMPLETED	SCREEN TIME HRS USED	TOTAL SCREEN TIME
SPACE PIONEERS	95%	12.42	10.42
TIME TRAVELERS	95%	12.00	10.50
COSMIC EXPLORERS	95%	11.40	10.90
EINSTEIN'S GIRLS	95%	13.50	12.00
JAPAN JOURNEYERS	95%	13.55	12.05
THE SMASH	95%	14.00	12.50
AUSSIE ASTRONAUTS	95%	13.50	12.50
ENGLISH EXPLORERS	95%	14.00	13.50
THE WOW	95%	14.50	14.00
SPANISH SPRINTERS	95%	14.70	14.70

CONTEST NEWS: The Space Pioneers, Time Travelers, and Cosmic Explorers hold places 1, 2, and 3. Bonus awards of -0.5, -1.0, and -1.5 will be made for the best story and picture Any of the top seven teams could win prizes.

to present their stories. Like the last time, the meeting will take place in California. United States' teams could go in person or appear remotely. All the teams from abroad would do remote presentations.

We had 13 days to prepare our story. The *Cosmic Explorers* and our parents were planning to be there in person.

"Our mom told us that Milo and his gang are making the trip too," I said, rolling my eyes in annoyance, which I couldn't help.

"OK, team," said Jackson, "what do we pick for the best picture and story?"

We discussed all the places in the universe that we had traveled to.

"How about the twin star supernova explosions followed by the neutron star merger?" suggested Johari.

"I love the photos of the colorful nebula star forming gas clouds," offered Neddy.

"I think everyone will use those," objected Jackson. "We need something different, something unique."

"How about that weird, egg-shaped planet?" offered Helen.

Then Richie and VC started to bat an idea back and forth. Grandpa and Tom added some more to the idea. Then Neddy made some suggestions. That was it. We had our idea for a picture and a great story to go with it. We spent the next week putting it all together.

On August 26, we had a final *Room* meeting to review what we had assembled. Johari and I practiced the presentation for the meeting in California. We made final improvements to our story, and then we submitted it for the final part of the contest.

On August 29, the East Coast *Cosmic Explorer* kids, together with our moms, dads, Grandpa, and Grandma, met at the Hartford airport for our flight to California. Once again, we all had on our double masks and face shields, and the Drs. Q had allowed everyone to purchase extra seats if they felt they needed to add more space around themselves. Tom flew in from Washington, DC, and Johari, Jackson, their parents, and Helen were driving.

▬ ▬ ▬ ▬ ▬

The group that assembled at the TSI mansion was much smaller than in July. The *Space Pioneers* were there with their parents, including our uncle, who had come with Milo. *Einstein's Girls* and *The Wow* were there too. The other teams in the top 10 attended remotely.

That night out on the patio, in masks and with social distancing, we were served a fantastic dinner. We had a choice of lobster or steak. Somehow Milo and Richie appeared to have gotten both.

After dinner, there were welcoming speeches by the Qs. Doctor Quinna invited any of the contestants who wanted to say a few words to come up onstage. Grandpa went up and complimented the Qs on the success of TSI and the *Virtual World*, which, in its first weeks open to the public, had attracted millions of users.

He concluded by saying, "I think combining the *Virtual World* as a graphically based search engine with its social media features will become a major success."

After dinner, our family went down to the ocean for a walk. At nine o'clock, it was already midnight for us East Coasters, so we went back to our rooms to go to sleep.

▬ ▬ ▬ ▬ ▬

The next day was sunny and warm. After breakfast, we did the beach thing again. In the afternoon, we got cleaned up, and at 5:00 p.m., we went back to the patio for the final presentations and awards.

The teams presented in the order of our final standings, so the *Space Pioneers* were the first up onstage. Their picture and story were about the merging neutron stars. The *Time Travelers* were next. Their story and picture were about the oldest and most distant galaxy in the universe, which is now 32 billion light years away from us.

Then it was our turn. Johari and I went up on stage.

I started us off. "You all know about our *Planet Colorado Space Station*. It was the winning space station design, and we won the prize money and one bonus hour to subtract from our screen time. Then, when we stopped there during the final race to the *Big Bang*, we discovered that the whole planet was infested with giant insects. We must have accidentally brought some tiny insects or larvae with the seeds and green slime we used to make our planet livable. The insects had grown in size and number during the 490 million years between the time we had finished the space station and when we returned 7 billion years ago. We were penalized with half an hour added back to our screen time because the space station appeared to be unusable at the end of the *Universe Seven Billion Years Ago to Now* mission. But at the start of the next mission, we quickly formulated a plan."

Johari took over. "We ordered seeds for several known species of plants that work as natural insect repellents, like chamomile, citronella grass, and chrysanthemums. Then we time traveled to ten years earlier and planted them all around our headquarters so that ten years later, the plants had grown thick and lush. It protected our HQ from all those bugs so that the *Planet Colorado Space Station* was usable again."

"We decided," I took back over, "that the screenshots taken the day we ran from those insects were some of the most unusual pictures we had taken during the whole *race*." A screenshot from that day was projected on the screen. "We call our story *Survival of the Fittest*."

Everyone clapped, so I waited a moment and then went on. "The story of what happened and *why* was definitely one of the most interesting stories from our adventures. What happened on *Planet Colorado* is an important piece of the story of Charles Darwin's *Theory of Evolution* that has been repeated on Planet Earth many times."

"Do you remember the mission stop on Earth 201 million years ago?" asked Johari. "It was an extinction event on Earth that wiped out most of the dominant land animals and let the dinosaurs flourish for the next 134 million years. With little competition for resources, the dinosaurs took over the planet, becoming larger and more numerous over time. Then, 65 million years ago, an asteroid wiped out the land dinosaurs, eliminating the species that was preventing mammals from flourishing."

I summed up. "In his *Theory of Evolution,* Darwin presented a principle known as *Survival of the Fittest.* It suggests that the *fittest* or strongest species will dominate and rule the Earth. If something like an asteroid hitting Earth happens, it might wipe out the fittest, allowing a new fittest to take over."

"What happened on our *Planet Colorado* was an accidental experiment in *Survival of the Fittest,*" continued Johari. "On Earth today, insects are small in the presence of their predators, mainly birds. Another factor is that our atmosphere is only 21% oxygen today, but insects weren't always so small."

"Yeah," I agreed. "About 300 million years ago before birds evolved, the atmosphere was made up of over 30% oxygen. Conditions were good for the survival of insects. So, we have fossils from that period that show dragonflies with wingspans of 0.6 meters. That's a 2-foot wingspan, compared to just four inches now."

"With *Planet Colorado,*" took over Johari, "we accidentally transferred a number of insects to an environment where there were no bird pred-ators. We measured the oxygen atmosphere when we left 7 billion years ago, and it was 31%. So, in the 490 million years from the time we unknowingly brought the insects to *Planet Colorado,* their numbers and size grew without limitation."

"This great experiment, showing one of the basic principles of the *Theory of Evolution,* may have been accidental," I began in conclusion, "but on *Planet Colorado* 7 billion years ago, insects were the fittest. When we humans visited, we were definitely not the fittest. But because humans have evolved to be great at problem solving, we managed to figure out a way to keep our space station functioning. So, we were able to make the rest of our video about our personal lives and our space station construction from our headquarters."

"Who knows?" Johari added in conclusion. "Maybe if we keep going back to our space station, by today, we'd be the fittest on that planet just like we've become here on Earth. Thank you for listening."

We got applause from the audience and a standing ovation from our table, which was kinda embarrassing. We returned to our table and got a collection of hugs, kisses, high fives, and elbow bumps from all the team members and families.

The presentations went on down the list of the top 10 teams, each coming onstage or projecting their virtual presentations. All the stories and pictures were of things that we had also seen. Our picture and story were totally original.

With the presentations finished, dinner was served.

"I can't eat. I am way too nervous," Neddy said, expressing what we were all feeling.

"Me too," said VC.

Richie, who didn't seem nervous at all, proceeded to eat *his* food plus contributions from everyone at the table.

▰ ▰ ▰ ▰ ▰

At 8:00 p.m., Dr. Q and Doctor Quinna went onstage before dessert was served. Dr. Q tapped the microphone to get everyone's attention. He gave a speech like the one he made last year about us wonderfully talented kids, about family, and about science. "I am so glad to have the participation of teams from all around the world," he said.

Then he continued. "I want to announce that as of today, our *Virtual World* has over 50 million users. This brilliant concept was the invention of a team from last year, the *Cosmic Kids*. They are all here tonight as members of two of the top 10 competing teams, the *Cosmic Explorers* and the *Space Pioneers*. Stand up, kids, and take a bow."

Milo, VC, Neddy, and I all stood up and got a standing ovation from everyone on the patio. The screen on the stage now showed the groups from around the world, each one in its own square. They were clapping for us too.

Then he announced, "Ladies and gentlemen, the judges have made their decisions."

Dr. Q handed the microphone to Doctor Quinna, who announced, "The third-place winner of $100,000 in cash and $1 million in college scholarships goes to the *Time Travelers* from Vietnam. You will receive your check and certificates by mail." The screen onstage showed their team members all bowing, raising their arms in victory, and cheering.

Neddy whispered to me and the other kids, "That means we have at least a second-place finish."

After the *Time Travelers* had a chance to say a few words, Doctor Quinna continued. "The second-place winner of $250,000 in cash and $1 million in college scholarships goes to the *Space Pioneers* from the East Coast region of the United States."

Milo, Svetlana, and company all screamed and headed for the stage.

"My brain is totally fried," said Neddy, "but unless our story was a total bust, I don't think any team but us could have a lower screen time than the *Space Pioneers*."

The *Space Pioneers* got their congratulations, a check, and scholarship certificates. Svetlana and Milo each made a short speech to thank the Drs. Q and the other teams.

Then Dr. Q. took over. "The grand-prize winner of $1 million in cash and $1 million in college scholarships goes to . . ."

He paused dramatically and looked around the room. My heart was pounding. My teammates were frozen in time at the edge of their seats. Grandpa, Helen, and Tom were each holding their breath.

Then the lights went out on the patio and all over the mansion, and the projector was turned off. We were plunged into total darkness. There were no lights anywhere to be seen.

Dr. Q started to speak. "Before announcing the winner, I wanted to show you my favorite picture in the universe. Look to your right," he instructed.

As our eyes adjusted to the dark, we saw millions of stars that were hidden by the normal lights around us.

"Wow," whispered Neddy, who was sitting next to me, "it's so beautiful."

"And you can see the bright region of the Milky Way slanting down into the trees," added VC, who was sitting on the other side.

"So, there it is," came Dr. Q's voice, "our amazing universe. You can see our home galaxy, the Milky Way, standing out among all the stars. So, what do I think is the most unusual thing in that universe? I think it is us humans. I think it is us here on this small planet who can look up and behold our universe. We, who can imagine the vastness of that universe and its beginnings in a *Big Bang* 13.8 billion years ago.

"So," continued Dr. Q., "the winning story and picture for the best thing in our race to the *Big Bang* is about *us*. It's about how we got to be here. One of our teams had a brilliant idea for their space station. We awarded that team the top prize for the *Regionals* competition along with a bonus of one hour to subtract from their screen time."

I started to let myself think that we must have won. I kept holding my breath.

"But then," added Dr. Q., "their space station turned out to be unusable. Even though they came up with a solution that impressed us, the initial attempt ended in failure."

Uh oh. Now I was thinking that we lost, and my heart sank.

"But this team recognized a wonderful piece of science in their failure. They saw a fantastic example of the kind of events that have allowed humans to evolve on Planet Earth. They recognized a vivid example of one of the key principles of the *Theory of Evolution*. They witnessed a perfect example of the *Survival of the Fittest*."

I could hear the gasps of my teammates, my sister, and my family as we all realized that we *had* won.

"So, my friends, I am happy to announce," Dr. Q said in a loud voice, "that the winning team is the team that showed us their wonderful picture of the fittest species on *Planet Colorado*, the insects grown to enormous size. The humans were the less fit species for that environment, and they had to run for their lives. I choked with laughter when I saw the picture. And they told us how that story has parallels here on Earth, where the events and changes in environment over billions of years have made us humans the surviving fittest."

The lights went back on. "Our winning team is the *Cosmic Explorers*!" Everyone started clapping as Dr. Q went on. "Come on up here, *Cosmic Explorers*, and get your grand-prize. Bring your families too."

I was in a fog and could barely hear the screaming and clapping going on all around me. We went onstage, and speeches were given. We thanked Dr. Q and Doctor Quinna. I kinda remember Grandpa giving a speech about how he had known the Qs for a long time and was very happy about their success. Then Neddy added that Grandpa had known *us* a long time too, and she hoped he was glad about *our* success. Everyone laughed at that.

By 11:00 p.m., happy but exhausted, we all headed upstairs to bed.

But that's not quite the end of our story. Before we went to our separate rooms, Neddy, VC, Johari, and I were together in the hall.

With a worried look on her face, Neddy asked, "Lizzy, could this pandemic be one of those events that knocks off the dominant species, us humans?"

"Come on, Neddy," I answered, "that's not going to happen."

Johari added, "We solved the problem of the insects, and look how quickly humans are finding a vaccine to help us survive Covid-19."

"This thing has been scary," Neddy said.

"Yes," I agreed, "but doesn't it already feel like everything will be back to normal soon? The social distancing and mask wearing has slowed down the infection rate, and we will all be vaccinated soon."

VC, who was listening quietly, said, "You guys have given me a cool idea. Let me think about it overnight. If it still seems good in the morning, I'll tell you about it."

We hugged each other, high fived, and fist bumped. Then we all went to our rooms for the night. I don't think I stopped smiling for a minute, even after I fell asleep.

EPILOGUE
THE COSMIC KIDS
COVID-19 EXPEDITIONS
(SEPTEMBER)

EPILOGUE 1

THE COSMIC KIDS COVID-19 EXPEDITION 1: INFECTION

(AS TOLD BY VC)

The contest was spectacular. Winning all that money for our families and college scholarships for us was incredible. To quote Johari, beating the teams from all over the world was "the GOAT." To quote Milo, '"It was awesome!"

His team didn't win first place, but he was very happy that he and Svetlana's family won second, and that *his* family members were the winners. We are all home now, but we are not back to the old pandemic routines. The TV stations and newspapers were calling every day to get members of our team for interviews. It was crazy time, but we still had work to do. We had a great new project.

This is what happened. On our final night in California, we went back to our rooms after all of the announcements. We were all totally wired after winning the contest. Everything after the announcement that we had won was kinda a blur.

We went up onstage and were congratulated by Dr. Q and Doctor Quinna. They gave us the biggest check for a million dollars that I had ever seen. I mean it was physically big, like three feet long. And we got certificates for the scholarships. We each got to say a few words. Then we were back on the patio getting congratulated by all the other kids and families.

At eleven o'clock, we headed to our rooms. But who could sleep? So Neddy and I got together in my room. We laughed and talked and jumped on the bed. At one in the morning, we had a massive pillow fight, where I knocked Neddy off the bed three times, and she knocked me off four times. Then we fell down, exhausted.

"We are gonna be so depressed when we get home," said Neddy. "What are we gonna do with ourselves without the team meetings and the *Virtual World* adventures? Going back to the pandemic lockdown routines and remote school is going to be awful. It is too depressing to think about."

Then my idea started floating back to the top of my brain. "Let's not stop," I said. "We can start something new and fantastic at home."

I told her my plan. Neddy added to it. We tossed it back and forth.

By four o'clock in the morning, we knew exactly what we would do. At six we woke Papa and Grandma up and told them. They loved it. At 7:00 a.m., we were dressed and downstairs for the meeting with the Qs that Papa had arranged.

Papa started off with our proposal. "We all think your *Virtual World* is wonderful. VC and Neddy have an idea that could add to the publicity that you have created with the contest, but they need some help from you."

"We would like to use the *Virtual World* to make videos for kids," I started. "Kids all over the world are suffering during the pandemic. We have social isolation and school closings. We don't get enough information to really understand the disease, and how we are going to be saved by a vaccine. And there is this too. How the virus uses our body to make duplicates of itself, and how some of the vaccines work, are really interesting. It is a great lesson in how our body works and uses the genetic information in DNA."

"So," Neddy jumped in, "we would like to make videos using the *Virtual World* about the Covid-19 pandemic. Videos that kids can understand. We could go on expeditions to track the virus in the body. We could do screenshot video captures of our activities and put them together into videos. And other kids could use the *Virtual World* for their own expeditions."

"That's our idea," I concluded. "But we need your help. We need your staff to add all the art assets and information that we will need to the *Virtual World* software. Can they add the insides of a human body, the virus, how the virus interacts with the body's cells, how the virus is transmitted from one person to another, and how the vaccines work? If you do that, we can produce the videos."

"I think that is a wonderful idea," said Doctor Quinna.

Dr. Q agreed and said we could start working on it in two weeks. Then at noon, we were on an airplane heading home.

▄ ▄ ▄ ▄ ▄

We decided that this would be a family project with the original *Cosmic Kids* team. So, *Milo the Missing* came back, and it was Milo, Neddy, Lizzy, me, and Papa on the video production team. Jackson and Johari promised they'd be there to consult if we needed them, but we all agreed it was better if we could do this job together in person. We knew we were going to have to fight with Milo about letting Svetlana help, but, honestly, she was pretty cool. And since Milo had basically joined her bubble, we thought maybe we could all just smoosh our bubbles together like two neutron stars. Hopefully, it wouldn't turn us into a black hole!

We agreed to start by producing two videos. The first was on the Covid-19 infection, and the second was on the vaccine. On September 15, we got an email from Doctor Quinna telling us that the *Virtual World* was ready for our project. That afternoon, we started an expedition called *Infection* to find out how Papa got sick.

"Let's start the video by reenacting my visit to the ice cream shop," said Papa. "That was six days before I got sick. It was the only time that I was out of the house in the two weeks before the virus hit me. It must have happened there."

So, we got Papa and his friend George to play out the scene in the real world, while we shot the video.

Papa set the scene outside the ice cream shop as he remembered it. He was at a table eating doughnuts, and George was coming out of the shop. Papa told us he had removed his mask outside to eat the doughnuts.

Scene from "Animated Coronavirus Story for Kids: How Grandpa got Covid-19."
The STARDUST MYSTERY YouTube Channel

"Grandpa!" Lizzy exclaimed. "I can't believe after all you have said to us about being careful that you broke quarantine to eat doughnuts."

"Yeah," I agreed. "And *four* doughnuts? Bad Papa."

"Very, very bad Grandpa," added Milo and Neddy.

"OK, OK, I get the message," said Papa. "You kids are right. Bad Grandpa. But we can use my mistake to find out how I got sick from the Covid-19 virus."

We videotaped as Grandpa directed the scene.

"There is someone coming out of the ice cream shop," I observed a short time later.

"Hi, Peter," this guy said to Papa.

"Oh, hi George," Papa answered, looking up from the doughnuts. "How're you doing?"

"I'm not feeling too well," said George, who then proceeded to sneeze and cough violently. "I had better go."

"Feel better," Papa called as George walked away.

"Looks like his sneeze didn't get to you, Papa," I observed. "You were more than 6 feet away, and I think it mostly landed on the table."

"We can't be sure, VC," responded Papa.

That's when we switched over to using the *Virtual World* assets for our video. We were in the *Cosmic Egg* to see a scene showing how a sneeze from an infected person could transmit the virus to someone else.

"Lizzy," commanded Papa, "please change our size down to the size of tiny aerosol droplets. Reduce our size by 1 million. That's micron size."

"Aye, aye, sir," Lizzy answered as she typed into the computer. "I am on it."

I got a little dizzy as our ship got smaller and smaller.

Neddy piloted the ship near the face of the soon-to-be-infected person representing Papa. We were looking for droplets. "Grandpa, you are right," said Neddy. "There are still plenty of tiny droplets in the air." She pulled our ship up close to one.

"Awesome," observed Milo. "I'll bet there are coronavirus particles in the droplets."

We were shooting the scene as though the *Virtual World* person was actually Papa.

"OK, kids," said Papa, "let's fly over to my nose and see if I got any of the droplets."

Neddy flew us near Papa's face, and we could see the particles going into his nose and mouth. "Just as I suspected," declared Papa. "I was inhaling lots of the tiny, infected droplets."

"Let's follow the droplets and see what happens," suggested Milo.

Neddy piloted the ship, flying up Papa's nose, following the droplets.

It got dark as soon as we got inside Papa's head, and we had to turn on our lights to see. We worked our way through a forest of Papa's nose hairs. Then we got to a large cave.

"This is my larynx," said Papa. "Let's keep going."

We passed through Papa's larynx and then got to a large pipe that went downward. The walls of the pipe were lined with bumps that had little hairs sticking out and some fluid on the surface.

"Wow, this is way cool," declared Lizzy. "Where are we?"

"We're in the trachea," called Neddy. "VC and I got the *Navigation* system going. The computer screen indicates where we are in the body."

"The red X is where we are," I explained. "And the label says it's the trachea."

"Right, agreed Papa. "The trachea is also called the windpipe. That pipe carries air to my lungs. These mounds are mucus <u>cells</u>, and the fluid is mucus."

"What is this stuff that looks like hair?" asked Milo. "Why is it in your windpipe?"

"The hair is called cilia," answered Papa. "It traps dust and foreign particles so they don't get into my lungs."

"I don't see any of the droplets or virus particles," I observed.

"Neddy," called Papa, "just park the ship for a while so we can see if any droplets get here. Lizzy, please advance time."

"Look," said Milo after a short wait. "Some of the droplets are starting to appear, and some are sticking to the mucus cells and cilia."

"Neddy," requested Papa, "please launch your drone so we can get a close-up look."

"Some of the individual virus particles are getting out of the droplets," I said.

"Cool," observed Lizzy. "One of the things sticking out on the virus just grabbed that little nub on the mucus cell."

"Lizzy," said Papa, "go forward slowly in time so we can see what happens next."

"Aye, aye, sir," Lizzy responded with a salute. "Advancing time by one hour every 10 minutes."

"Wow," I observed, "the virus is going all the way into the mucus cell."

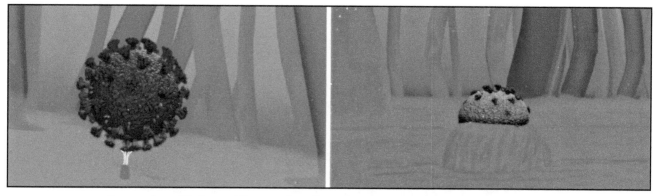

Scenes from "Animated Coronavirus Story for Kids: How Grandpa got Covid-19."
The STARDUST MYSTERY YouTube Channel

"Lots of other virus particles are doing the same thing," added Milo.

"Look," I called. "The surface of the cell is clear. The virus particles that landed are now all inside the mucus cell."

"Lizzy," said Papa, "continue advancing time until we see what happens next."

A short time later, Milo said, "Oh, wow, Grandpa, lots of virus particles are popping out all over your mucus cells."

"There are lots more particles than the few that went into the cell," observed Neddy.

"That's right, kids," said Papa. "The viruses got duplicated in my cell."

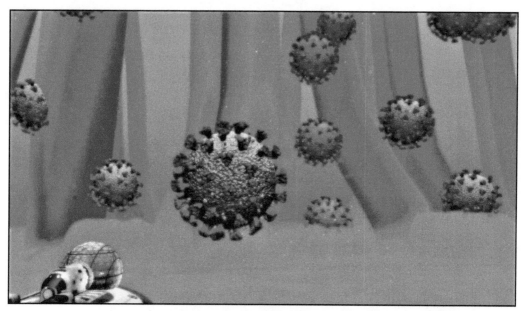

Scene from "Animated Coronavirus Story for Kids: How Grandpa got Covid-19."
The STARDUST MYSTERY YouTube Channel

"Wow," I said, "the virus has turned Papa's mucus cell into a factory to make duplicates of the virus particles."

"Yes, that's right," responded Grandpa. "Our different body cells are little factories that produce things that the body requires. When some object is needed, the cell creates a molecule called messenger RNA, or mRNA, with the required code for the object. The mRNA goes to the cell's factory, called ribosomes, which uses the code to create copies of the object. That clever Covid-19 virus presented its RNA to my cell's ribosomes, and they obey by churning out lots of virus copies. The virus can either get into the cell or it can fuse with the cell wall and inject its RNA into the cell."

"That's a pretty smart virus that gets your body's own manufacturing system to do all the work," added Lizzy.

"Grandpa," asked Neddy, "where is your immune defense? Your body needs to call in the troops."

"That's a good question," answered Papa. "I asked Uncle Will about that when I got sick. As the only doctor in the family, he gets all the medical questions. He explained what happens. In among the mucus cells are cells of the immune system that sense when anything foreign has invaded my body and produce antibodies. The antibodies seek out the virus and attach to the structures that stick out of their surfaces. With the antibodies hanging on to them, the virus can't attach to the surface of my mucus cells. They can't get inside my cells, and so they can't get reproduced.

"Neddy and VC," Papa suggested, "see if you can find an image of an antibody so we know what to look for."

Neddy found a picture of the antibody that would be released in the windpipe, and Milo and Lizzy went over to the windows to look for them.

"Papa," I said, "I see some of those antibody things attacking one of the virus cells. But most of the antibodies are ignoring them."

"Yes," responded Papa. "Uncle Will said it takes days before the antibodies recognize the Covid-19 virus as the enemy."

Neddy piloted us over for a closer look.

"There is just one single virus particle being attacked," said Lizzy.

"Yeah," agreed Milo, "but there is a virus particle near it that has no antibodies, and it is attaching to Grandpa's mucus cell. And I can see lots of virus particles and very few antibodies that are attacking them."

"Yeah, Grandpa," added Lizzy, "it doesn't look like there are enough antibodies to save you."

"Papa," I reasoned, "the fact that you got sick suggests that the antibody protection didn't happen fast enough."

"That must be right," agreed Papa.

"Grandpa," called Lizzy, "the virus particles are moving further down your windpipe. Can we follow them?"

"Yes," replied Papa. "Neddy, please move us down the trachea."

"Aye, aye, sir," Neddy said in an excellent imitation of her sister. "I am on it."

"We are at a fork in the windpipe," observed Lizzy.

"Yes," said Papa, "those are my two bronchial tubes that take the air to my two lungs."

"Let's keep going," urged Milo.

Neddy made the left turn into one of Papa's bronchi. This part of his airway looked clean, so we stopped and advanced time. A short time later, the virus particles appeared. We kept going into smaller and smaller tubes. Finally, we arrived at a cave-like enclosure with red walls that moved in and out. It was a dead end.

"Our navigation system says we were in an alveolus," I reported. "And here is a diagram of where we are."

"Right," agreed Papa. "Alveoli are the lungs' air sacks, where oxygen from the air goes into the blood, and carbon dioxide from the blood goes into the air. Lizzy, start going forward in time so we can see what happens next."

A short time later, the virus particles started to arrive in huge numbers.

"Look," observed Milo, "the virus is taking over the whole alveolus. It is all over the surface."

"Grandpa," asked Lizzy, "how did you manage to breathe with all the virus particles coating the surface?"

"That was the problem, Lizzy," replied Grandpa. "I couldn't breathe very well."

"Look now," added Lizzy. "The whole air sack is filling with fluid."

"This is getting bad," said Neddy.

"Really bad," I agreed.

Scenes from "Animated Coronavirus Story for Kids: How Grandpa got Covid-19."
The STARDUST MYSTERY YouTube Channel

"Wow," said Milo, "now the whole air sack is filled with fluid."

"The lung alveoli filling with fluid is called pneumonia," explained Grandpa. "That is when I got rushed to the hospital and put on a ventilator."

"Now we know how you got sick, Papa," I said.

"Wow," said Neddy, "that virus is really dangerous."

"Yes, it is," agreed Papa.

"Good job, kids," he added. "Tomorrow, let's do the second expedition to find out how the vaccine is supposed to work to save us."

EPILOGUE 2

THE COSMIC KIDS COVID-19 EXPEDITION 2: VACCINE

(AS TOLD BY MILO)

I am back working with my old *Cosmic Kids* team, and I am really happy about that. Besides not being on the winning team, there were a bunch of things that I missed. I missed having G-Pa as my coach, and believe it or not, I missed fighting with Lizzy. I also missed writing the journal chapters. But this new activity is really awesome. I am in charge of planning the video on the Covid-19 vaccine.

We invited Uncle Will, who is a doctor, to the *Room* meeting with the *Cosmic Kids* to plan the video production. G-Pa was there too.

"My mom is going to take part in a vaccine trial," Lizzy informed us. "She will get one shot three days from now and a second shot 28 days later. She said she is testing a vaccine based on mRNA technology. Can you tell us about it, Uncle Will?"

"Of course," answered Uncle Will. "The mRNA technology is the latest thing in vaccines. It is really incredible. Up until now, most vaccines have been developed using dead or weakened forms of the virus. When injected, the body's immune system develops antibodies and other cells that will fight the real virus if it ever appears. Developing such vaccines has, in the past, taken up to eight years."

"Wow," said Neddy, "that's a really long time. How did they get ready to test a vaccine on my mom in six months?"

"All the doctors and scientists were working very hard to get something ready really fast that works," Uncle Will explained. "But a vaccine using the mRNA technology is actually easier to develop. It is really cool stuff, and it's going to change all the vaccines we make in the future."

"So how does it work?" asked VC.

"The keys to understanding how the virus reproduces and how the vaccines will work," explained Uncle Will, "are huge molecules called RNA and DNA. Here are some pictures of them."

Uncle Will screen shared

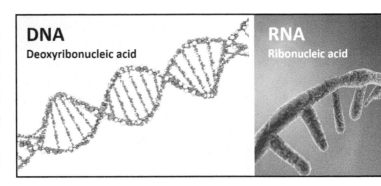

DNA
Deoxyribonucleic acid

RNA
Ribonucleic acid

the pictures and told us about them. "They are both large molecules made of carbon, hydrogen, oxygen, nitrogen, and phosphorus atoms. Different combinations of these atoms in different sequences create the genetic code describing how an organism or virus is built. For us humans, all the information on how to create each piece of us is contained in our DNA. It is a two-strand molecule arranged in a twisted pair. We get one strand from our mother and the other from our father. The virus doesn't have a mother and a father, so for the coronavirus, a single-strand RNA molecule contains its genetic code.

"Do you remember how the Covid-19 virus reproduced itself in Grandpa's body?" asked Uncle Will.

"Yeah," said VC. "It got into one of Papa's cells and got his cell to make virus copies using the virus's own RNA as the code for how to produce it."

"Yes, that's right," responded Uncle Will, who had made us a diagram. "Our body's cells are little factories that produce things that the body needs. For example, on the left, the diagram shows a cell from the stomach that produces the chemical pepsin, needed for digesting food. The instructions for making pepsin are in a small piece of the DNA genetic code, and every cell has your DNA in a place called the cell nucleus. The nucleus creates a molecule called messenger RNA, mRNA, with the required piece of code for producing pepsin. The mRNA is sent to the cell's factory, called the ribosomes, and it manufactures the pepsin. If a virus had invaded one of those cells, as shown in the middle diagram, the factory would manufacture virus copies."

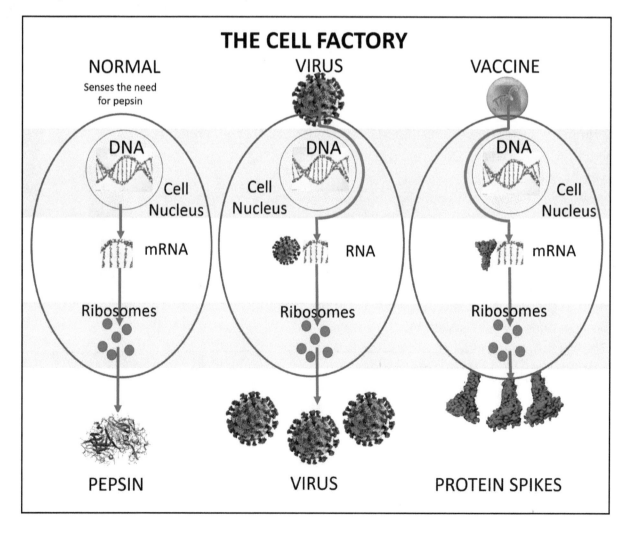

"Oh, I get it," I said. "The clever virus hijacks your cell's factory. It presents its RNA to your cell's ribosomes, and the factory responds by manufacturing lots of virus copies like you show in the middle diagram."

"There is another way the virus can invade a cell," added G-Pa. "It can attach to the cell surface and transmit its instructions for making virus copies directly into the cell."

"Right," responded Uncle Will. "Well, our doctors and scientists are just as smart as a virus. They took a small part of the virus's RNA and made their own mRNA. It was the code for building the protein spikes that appear all over the virus's surface. Then they figured out how to get that little section of mRNA inside human cells so that the cell's ribosome factory will make copies of those spike proteins. That's the diagram on the right."

"Now I get it," said Lizzy. "When lots of spike protein copies are made, the body's immune system senses these foreign objects and learns how to attack and destroy the spikes and the infected cell. So, when the real virus shows up with those same protein spikes, our bodies know how to deal with it."

"Yes, Lizzy," said Uncle Will. "The immune system will have antibodies and killer T-cells that were created in response to the vaccine. They remain for months to fight the real virus if it should appear. As long as your immune system remembers the spike protein attack, it will use the same strategy to attack the complete virus, which has those same spike proteins."

When Uncle Will finished explaining, I said, "That is awesome. The vaccine gets your body to produce just the spikes, and you can't get sick from them. But the spikes get your immune system ready to fight the complete virus, which has the same spikes."

"Another thing that is awesome," added Neddy, "is that scientists can pick out just the piece of the virus's RNA that is the code for making protein spikes."

"Thanks, Uncle Will," I said. "I think we got the story straight and are ready to make our video."

■ ■ ■ ■ ■

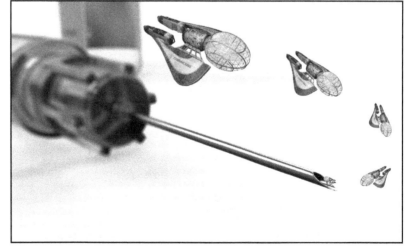

We waited for Aunt Debbie to get her vaccine shot and went with her to videotape the event. For the next part of the video, we logged on to the *Virtual World* and went to the *Cosmic Egg*. We reduced our size and flew toward a needle with the vaccine that was about to be injected into a person's arm.

Then for our video, we pretended that we were following the vaccine as it worked in my aunt's body.

As we approached the opening at the end of the needle, Neddy and VC were loading some of the pictures of what we were looking for into their computer.

"OK, guys," announced Neddy, "take a look at the screen. The immunization strategy involves reproducing the Covid-19 protein spikes in my mom's body. The spikes without the rest of the virus won't make her sick, but they will get her immune system ready to fight the real Covid-19 virus. This is what the protein spikes look like." She pointed to her computer screen.

Lizzy took over the controls so I could see. Then Neddy brought up the next image of the mRNA that was the code for building a protein spike.

"The mRNA molecule looks like a short piece of the virus RNA," remarked Grandpa.

"There was one more thing that we need to show you," said VC, "before we follow the vaccine into Aunt Debbie's arm. The mRNA molecule is not very stable. It has to be kept very cold during storage before it is used. It also has to be wrapped in an oily coating so that the body won't chew it up before it could do its work. So, we need to look for droplets containing the mRNA."

"OK, now we are ready to go," said Neddy. "Milo, take us into the needle." We entered the needle that was already filled with vaccine. "The nurse is now injecting the vaccine," Neddy observed.

We floated along in the vaccine fluid. Eventually, we were able to view the droplets, containing strands of mRNA, hit the surface of a cell. We watched as the coated mRNA particles started to stick to the cell's surface.

"Neddy," I said, "why don't you launch the drone with the camera so that we can get a closer look using your large computer screen? Yeah, much better."

"Look," said Lizzy, "the mRNA is moving out of the protective coating and burrowing into the cell."

"According to Uncle Will," said Neddy, "this is the important part. Once the mRNA is inside a cell, the cell's ribosomes will take the code in the mRNA and start churning out protein spikes that are identical to those on the virus. Some of them will stick out on the cell surface."

"Right," announced VC. "It's building the protein spike copies because that is the instruction or code in the piece of mRNA that they extracted from the virus."

"You kids have got the story straight," complimented G-Pa. "Now you have reached the stage that is important. The foreign protein spikes are appearing on the cell's surface. They are going to fool the vaccinated person's immune system into sensing that it is being attacked by the Covid-19 virus. Because it is a simulation of an attack and not the real thing, the person won't get sick, so the immune system has plenty of time to respond.

"Milo," asked G-Pa, "please advance the time to see how the person's immune system responds."

"You got it, G-Pa," answered Milo. "Advancing one hour every minute."

"I got a great idea," announced Neddy. "Let's put on our breathing helmets and go out and see the protein spikes. We can see if any antibodies arrive."

I stayed at the controls while the girls went out and started to chase each other around the protein spikes.

Soon, the three-pronged antibodies started to appear, and some attached themselves to the protein spikes.

"It looks like one of those antibodies is going to attack me," yelled VC.

Neddy and Lizzy had already figured that out and started running back to the ship. They yelled a warning to VC, and she quickly followed.

When the girls were safely inside, Grandpa said. "We should have predicted the attack on you girls. You are foreign objects, so the immune system is going to attack you, as well as the protein spikes. They are also starting to attack the ship too."

"Now I see how the vaccine works," I observed. "It created the antibodies to attack the protein spikes. Those protein spikes are what the virus uses to get inside a cell to reproduce. So, if any virus particles got into the body, the antibodies that are ready and waiting would hang onto the spikes, so the virus wouldn't be able to get inside a cell to reproduce."

"Not like your case, Grandpa," observed VC, "where your immune system produced hardly any antibodies in time to save you."

Uncle Will added this information: "After a while, a vaccinated person's immune system will get its cleanup crew into action. Killer T-cells and other immune system cells will destroy all of the protein spikes and the infected cells. What will be left in the person's body will be the antibodies, memory B-cells that had the recipe for producing more of the right kind of antibodies, and killer T-cells with simulated experience combating the Covid-19 virus."

"After the second shot," Uncle Will continued, "the person's immune system would be ready to spring into action to disable any Covid-19 virus particle immediately. They wouldn't be able to get into a cell to reproduce."

"It would have been great," I suggested, "if G-Pa and Uncle Ken had the vaccine early enough to prevent them from getting sick."

"But we can't complain," concluded G-Pa. "They developed this mRNA vaccine in record time. Only 5 percent of the people who got the vaccine in the trials got sick, and those who did get sick only had mild cases of the virus."

"How long will a person be safe after being vaccinated?" I asked.

"It's possible," responded Uncle Will, "that in the months after vaccination, the number of antibodies and killer T-cells will drop. But the immune system also contains special memory B-cells and memory T-cells that might retain information about the coronavirus for years or even decades."

GRANDPA'S GLOSSARY

Chapter 1: Feeling Low-Down

<u>Virtual World:</u> Virtual worlds, also known as virtual environments, use computer technology to create a simulated world that a user can explore and interact with, while creating a feeling as if he were in that world. The representation of the user in that world is called an <u>avatar</u>. The user can even wear goggles to make it appear that he or she is surrounded by the 3-D virtual world. That is called virtual reality.

<u>The Stardust Mystery:</u> The Stardust Mystery illustrated science storybook is a companion to the MissionKT and Building the Universe video games, <u>TheStardustMystery.com</u> web page, and the STARDUST MYSTERY YouTube channel. It follows the lives of cousins Lizzy, Milo, VC, and Neddy as they unravel the Stardust Mystery. Their adventures take them across time during the evolution of the Universe and the history of Planet Earth in the Cosmic Egg time, space, and size-change travel ship. They must figure out how everyone alive is made of the same Stardust that was once in the bodies of Albert Einstein and the Last T-Rex. They must find out what Stardust is, and how, when, and where it was created. As the Cosmic Kids team, the cousins enter The Science and The Future Contest, held by the mysterious Dr. Q The winners will be taken on a trip around the moon! What could be a better gift for the grandfather they love, a former NASA astronaut? Along the way, they visit Einstein, dinosaurs, and even the Big Bang. To win, they'll have to use their brains to answer the many science questions, but they'll also have to use their hearts to come together to solve the problems of family.

<u>Covid-19 Coronavirus:</u> COVID-19 is a disease produced by a coronavirus that can cause an infection of the respiratory system (sinuses, nose, throat, windpipe, and lungs). The disease spreads mainly by sharing of the coronavirus particles through person-to-person transmission (most often in airborne droplets containing the virus particles). Coronaviruses are named for the distinct crown-like protein spikes on their surface. They cause many different diseases, including Covid-19 and the common cold.

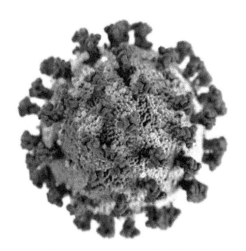

Corona Virus image, created by Alissa Eckert, MSMI, Dan Higgins, MAMS, From The Centers For Disease Control And Prevention

A virus is a particle one-hundredth the size of most bacteria, too small to be seen with an optical microscope. Virus particles consist of their genetic code material in the form of DNA or RNA, a protein coat which surrounds and protects the genetic material and in some cases an outside oily layer. The double strand DNA or single strand RNA molecules contain the genetic code for the virus's structure. The code is written in the order of atoms and molecules that make up the DNA or RNA.

Some scientists consider viruses to be living organisms because they carry their genetic code, reproduce, and evolve through natural selection. Others disagree because viruses lack cell structure and cannot independently reproduce. To make copies of themselves, they employ the capability of living cells to reproduce organic components from RNA-coded instructions. They invade the cells of living organisms and induce the cell's own mechanisms to reproduce the virus based on the virus's RNA genetic code. Viruses can pull off this trick with cells of animals, plants, and microorganisms such as bacteria. When infected, the host cells are forced to rapidly produce thousands of identical copies of the original virus.

One of the vaccines to combat the Covid-19 Coronavirus (the mRNA vaccine) uses the virus's own trick to defeat it. A small piece of the virus's RNA with the code to produce the protein spikes is presented to the body's cells. The cells reproduce lots of copies of the protein spikes. These virus pieces get the body's immune system primed to combat the virus without any danger of producing the disease.

Pandemic: A pandemic is a wide area spread of an infectious disease over multiple continents or worldwide, affecting a substantial number of people.

Chapter 2: The Race to the Big Bang

Gravitational Wave: Like black holes, gravitational waves are predicted by Einstein's General Theory of Relativity. They are disturbances in space itself (stretching and contracting) that travel at the speed of light away from the event that caused them.

LIGO: The National Science Foundation funded the development of the Laser Interferometer Gravitational-Wave Observatory (LIGO) to detect gravitational waves. Two of them were built far apart, and a disturbance must be seen simultaneously by both to be identified as a real event. The first event, detected in 2015, was believed to be produced by two black holes merging. In the summer of 2017, LIGO detected a gravitational wave produced by the merging of two neutron stars. Additional measurements from detectors of visible and other radiation wavelengths indicated that that event had produced a weight of gold equal to the weight of planet Earth. Neutron star merging appears to be a very important event that produces our heavy atoms.

Room Communication App: A fictional internet communication software application that permits multiple users to hear and see each other and share their digital device screens. It is like the real app called Zoom.

Acceleration Due to Gravity: Gravity is a force of attraction between all physical objects. If an object on Earth is dropped or thrown, the force of gravity between Planet Earth and the object will cause it to accelerate towards Earth. On Earth, the acceleration (rate of change of velocity) due to this gravitational force is 9.8 meters per second per second. That means that the velocity changes by 9.8 meters per second every second. The acceleration due to gravity on the moon is 1/6 the value on Earth. The value depends on the mass and radius of the Earth or moon.

Galileo's Experiment: There is a popular story, which may or may not be true, that in 1589, the Italian scientist Galileo Galilei had dropped two objects of different masses from the Leaning Tower of Pisa to demonstrate that their fall time was the same. This showed that the objects had the same acceleration due to gravity. This observation disproved Aristotle's theory of gravity, which states that objects fall at speeds that depend on their masses. We now know that Galileo's theory was correct.

Chapter 3: Svetlana on my Mind

MissionKT: MissionKT is a multiplayer video game set in the last days of the dinosaurs. The players have scientific instruments with which to measure properties of the objects in the game (chemical composition, mass, velocity, temperature, density, etc.). The game is available on the video game website, store.steampowered.com.

Made of the Same Stardust: Stardust pieces are atoms created in the explosive death of stars. We each have carbon atom stardust that once was in the bodies of Albert Einstein and the Last T-Rex. This is how we got them. Einstein and the T-Rex exhaled carbon dioxide made from carbon in their bodies. Some of that carbon dioxide is still in the atmosphere today, and some of the carbon has been used to grow fruits, vegetables, and animals. The food we eat contains large numbers of carbon atoms that were once in Einstein, in each T-Rex, and in all other living things.

Number of Carbon Atoms in a Human: Start with the mass of an average 75 kilogram person, of which 18.5 percent of the mass is carbon. So, a person contains 13.9 kg or 13,900 grams of carbon. That would be 13,900/12 = 1,156 moles of carbon. A mole of carbon is a weight in grams equal to the atomic weight of the atom (where 12 is the atomic weight of the carbon atom that has 6 protons and 6 neutrons). One mole of any atom or molecule has the same number of atoms, and that number is called Avogadro's number (602 billion trillion) = 6.02×10^{23}. So, a 75 kilogram human will contain 1,156 x 6.02×10^{23} = 7×10^{26} carbon atoms, 7 followed by 26 zeros: 700,000,000,000,000,000,000,000,000.

Chapter 4: Cosmic Explorers

Submillimeter Observatory: These facilities employ telescopes that measure radiation from space in the submillimeter wavelength range (microwave and infrared regions of the spectrum). Their goal is to provide chemical composition data on cosmic gas clouds to investigate the formation of stars.

Chapter 5: Nearly Normal

Family Bubble: During the Covid-19 pandemic, groups of friends, family members, sports teams, business employees, etc. formed groups (bubbles) that could meet in person. Members of each bubble followed agreed-upon rules of safe behavior to reduce the risk of contracting Covid-19. They typically agreed to eliminate all non-protected contact with individuals outside the bubble.

Chapter 6: Qualifying Begins

Atoms: Every solid, liquid, or gas in our world is made of atoms. Most things, like water, people, trees, houses, or cars, are made of combinations of different kinds of atoms. But some substances like silver or gold or oxygen or carbon are made of only one kind of atom, and these are called chemical elements. The atom is the smallest unit that defines a chemical element. Anything made of atoms has mass, meaning that a force is necessary to make it go faster or slower, and it experiences a gravitational attraction to other masses. Atoms are very small. A single strand of human hair is almost 1 million carbon atoms wide. Atoms can be attached to one another in small units called molecules, in large crystals like diamond and salt, in mixtures of crystals, or in random arrangements in solids or liquids. You can see some of these arrangements in the animated Science Videos on the STARDUST MYSTERY YouTube channel. Milo, Lizzy, VC, Johari, and Neddy have starring roles in those videos. You can build atoms in the *Building the Universe* game available on Store.SteamPowered.com.

Some things in our world are not made of atoms. The most common is light, which consists of tiny particles called photons. Photons always move fast and have no mass. Some things are parts of atoms, like a beam of electrons in an electron microscope or an old television tube. And then there is *dark energy* and *dark matter*, which we think are out there in the universe but are not made of atoms. We are pretty sure they're there, but we don't yet know what they're made of.

The Big Bang: More than two thousand years ago, humans looked at all the things in the sky and decided that the universe consisted of the Earth at the center with the sun, moon, and stars all revolving around the Earth. In the fifteenth and sixteenth centuries, Copernicus and then Kepler and Galileo said that the universe has the sun as the center, and everything revolves around the sun. Then, in the nineteenth century the picture changed to the sun and planets revolving around the center of the Milky Way galaxy. In the early twentieth century, the work of Henrietta Leavitt and Edwin Hubble showed that the Milky Way galaxy was only a small part of the universe, which has billions more galaxies like the Milky Way. What's more, Hubble's measurements, and the predictions of Alexander Friedmann and Georges Lemaître, showed that the universe is expanding, with the most distant stars moving away from us the fastest.

Based on the Theory of Relativity, Lemaître made a bold prediction. He reasoned that if you follow the universe back in time, it gets smaller. The further back in time you look, the smaller it has to be. So, if the evolution of the universe were a movie showing its expansion, and you played it backwards, it would be contracting. The contraction of the universe would put it in one tiny super-dense point about 14 billion years ago. Lemaître pictured the expansion of the universe from that point as the hatching of "the *Cosmic Egg* exploding at the moment of the creation." Other scientists call this the *Big Bang* theory. Lemaître gave lectures explaining his theory, including at Princeton University, where Albert Einstein was in attendance. It was reported that Einstein said, "This is the most beautiful and satisfactory explanation of creation to which I have ever listened."

How do we know that the *Big Bang* theory is correct? Well, scientists can calculate what occurred as the universe expanded from that first point. They can make predictions about the concentrations of elements in the universe and about the leftover radiation from the earliest times, which can still be seen as the cosmic microwave background. They can predict the size of stars, galaxies and galaxy clusters, and the rate of the universe's expansion. Compared with the observations, the *Big Bang* theory is very accurate.

Supernova Star Explosion: Stars are bright because they are very hot due to nuclear fusion in which hydrogen atoms combine to form helium atoms. After billions of years, all of the hydrogen is consumed, and the star starts to cool and collapse toward the center. In big stars, the collapse leads to an explosion called a supernova, in which huge amounts of light and material are released. Supernovas are bright enough to be seen on Earth with the naked eye and can last for up to two years.

Nuclear Fusion: Nuclear fusion is what happens when two atoms come together and form a new larger atom. We can exist because nuclear fusion on our sun provides light and energy to our planet. On the sun, the main nuclear fusion reaction takes place when one hydrogen atom that has one proton and one neutron (^{2}H, called deuterium or heavy hydrogen) bangs into another hydrogen atom (^{3}H, called tritium) that has one proton and two neutrons. In order to fuse, they must bang into each other really hard, and that requires a temperature of 15 million degrees C. They fuse into a helium atom with

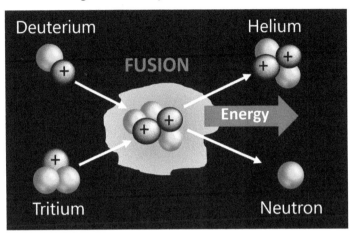

two protons and two neutrons (^{4}He), and the extra neutron comes out with lots of energy. All that energy is what keeps the sun burning bright.

Fusion of bigger atoms on our sun can form atoms like lithium with three protons, beryllium with four protons, and small amounts of bigger atoms. But really big stars can form big atoms in their cores, where the temperature is really hot. When a star uses all its hydrogen, it either becomes a white dwarf the size of Earth (like our sun would do), or if it is a big star, it collapses and forms a supernova. And in that supernova, conditions are hot enough (100 billion degrees C) to form atoms like iron that have twenty-six protons, and even uranium that has ninety-two protons.

Neutron Star Pair Merger: A neutron star is the collapsed core of a massive supergiant star, which had a total mass of between 10 and 25 solar masses. Except for black holes, and some hypothetical objects, neutron stars are the smallest and densest currently known class of stellar objects. It Is possible for a pair of such large stars (connected by the gravitational force) to form a pair of neutron stars. These neutron stars will circle each other, getting closer and closer together, until finally they merge in a supernova explosion. Such a merger was observed by LIGO in 2017. Other radiation sensors observed the production of massive amounts of heavy elements. The weight of gold produced was estimated to be equal to the weight of planet Earth. Neutron star pair mergers are now considered to be one of the major sources of heavy elements.

Metal Detector: Metal detectors are often seen at the shore, being used by beachcombers searching for lost metal objects like rings and watches. Its operation is relatively simple. The device puts out an electromagnetic wave signal that induces currents in any metal object underneath the device. These currents produce a return signal detected by the device, indicating the presence of a metal object.

Multi-Messenger Astronomy: The detection of the neutron star pair merger by LIGO and other detectors in 2017 is considered to be an excellent example of Multi-Messenger Astronomy. The messages arriving on Earth are the gravitational waves detected by LIGO and radiation (visible, infrared, ultraviolet, X-ray, and gamma ray) detected by other instruments. The combination of multi-messages provides information not available from a single observation. Such a combination was employed to identify the event as a neutron star pair merger.

Lightest Atoms: These are the atoms produced by supernovas of the first generation of gas stars occurring within the first few hundred million years after the Big Bang. Atoms between carbon (atomic number 6) and strontium (atomic number 38) were produced.

Heaviest Atoms: These are the atoms produced in the cores and subsequent supernovas of second and third generation stars occurring billions of years after the Big Bang. They were also produced in neutron star pair mergers. Atoms between zirconium (atomic number 40) and uranium (atomic number 92) were produced.

Quarks: Scientists discovered that besides the well-known building components for atoms (protons, neutrons, and electrons), there are over 200 other fundamental particles (including photons, W bosons, Z bosons, gluons, Higgs bosons, gravitons, muons, and neutrinos). In 1969 Murray Gell-Mann and George Zweig independently proposed that, just as atoms are composed of smaller particles, most elementary particles were actually composed of a smaller set of particles, too. These are called quarks. There are six types, or flavors, of quarks: up, down, strange, charm, bottom, and top. Protons are made of two up quarks and one down quark. Neutrons are made of two down quarks and one up quark.

Electrons: All atoms are made of the same three particles: electrons, protons, and neutrons. Electrons are tiny particles that have very little mass and a negative electrical charge. They were formed in the Big Bang.

Andromeda Galaxy: Andromeda is the nearest neighboring galaxy to our Milky Way galaxy. It is approximately 2.5 million light-years from Earth. Andromeda is a spiral galaxy (like the Milky Way) consisting of about 1 trillion stars. The Milky Way and Andromeda galaxies are expected to collide in around 4.5 billion years.

Chapter 8: Virtual Trip to the Moon

Force of Gravity: Gravity is the weakest of the four fundamental forces of nature. It is a force by which all things with mass (including ordinary objects, atoms, planets, stars, and galaxies) are attracted to one another. On Earth, gravity's pull on an object gives it weight. Gravity has an infinite range, although its effects become increasingly weaker as objects get further away. First Galileo, and then Sir Isaac Newton, predicted the inverse-square law of gravitation (the force is proportional to 1 divided by the distance between them squared). Newton proposed the following equation:

$$F = G*m(1)*m(2)/r^2,$$

where F is the force between two masses, m(1) and m(2), r is the distance between the centers of the masses, and G is the gravitational constant.

Gravity is more accurately described by the General Theory of Relativity proposed by Albert Einstein. Even light is affected by gravity in Einstein's theory.

Moon mass calculation: The circumference of the moon is 10,920 kilometers. The circumference is $2\pi r$ where r is the radius of the moon and $\pi = 3.14$. With the volume equal to $4/3\ \pi\ r^3$, we get the volume of the moon as 2.2×10^{25} cubic centimeters. Using the measured density of 3.34 grams/cm^3 and the formula Mass=density x volume, we get 7.35 x 10^{25} grams, or 7.35 x 10^{22} kilograms for the moon's mass. This is the known mass.

Barringer Meteorite Crater: This crater located in the Arizona desert is a well-preserved 50,000 year old impact feature. It is 1.2 kilometers in diameter and 170 meters deep. The rim of the crater rises 45 meters above the desert floor. It was formed when a large meteorite hit the Earth.

Chapter 9: Peculiar Things in the Solar System

Solar System Exploration: This NASA website at solarsystem.nasa.gov is an excellent source of data and images for all the objects in the solar system.

Mars Rover: The picture on pg. 52 is of the Mars Rover, Perseverance, that touched down on the surface of Mars on February 18, 2021. The Rover will be collecting samples of the Martian surface which will be sent back to Earth. When returned, the samples will be examined for any evidence of past life on Mars. Perseverance is the latest of 6 probes sent to Mars. The Curiosity Rover that landed in 2011 is still active.

Table of Planet Properties:

Planet	Radius Earth=1	Mass Earth=1	Surface Gravity (Earth = 1)	Surface Temperature Celsius	Average density (g/cm³)	Composition (in order of abundance)	Atmosphere Top two Molecules	Atmosphere Pressure surface	Orbit Period in Earth Days	Distance to the Sun {million km}
MERCURY	0.38	0.0558	0.378	430	5.44	Fe, Ni, Si	*	0	88	65
VENUS	0.95	0.815	0.903	698	5.24	Si, Fe, Ni	CO_2, N_2	91.78	225	108
EARTH	1.00	1	1	15	5.50	Si, Fe, Ni	N_2, O_2	1.00	365	150
MARS	0.53	0.1075	0.379	-68	3.94	Si, Fe, S	CO_2, N_2	0.01	687	212
JUPITER	11.20	317.83	2.54	-145	1.34	H, He	H_2, He	1.00	4,380	767
SATURN	9.42	95.147	1.16	-178	0.69	H, He	H_2, He	1.00	10,585	1,493
URANUS	4.01	14.54	0.919	-195	1.19	H, C, N, O	H_2, He	1.00	30,660	2,959
NEPTUNE	3.93	17.23	1.19	-200	1.66	H, C, N, O	H_2, He	1,000	60,190	4,477
PLUTO	0.19	0.002	0.063	-233	1.85	C, H, O	*	0.00	90,520	5,900
MOON	0.19	0.012	0.167	-23	3.30	O, Si, Al	*	0.00	27	150

Chapter 10: Peculiar Things in the Ocean

Titanic: The Titanic was a British luxury ocean liner launched in 1911. It was carrying more than 2,200 passengers and crew when it sank on its maiden voyage after hitting an iceberg. The ship was 269 meters long with a maximum width of 28.2 meters. The wreck of the Titanic was discovered in 1985 at a depth of 3.78 kilometers.

Chapter 11: Proving the Big Bang Theory

Professor Georges Lemaître: Georges Lemaître was a Belgian Catholic priest, mathematician, astronomer, and professor of physics at the Catholic University of Leuven. He was born in 1894 and died in

1966. In 1927 he published a revolutionary paper in which he proposed the concept of the expanding universe. Based on solutions of Einstein's General Relativity equations, Lemaître presented his "hypothesis of the primeval atom" or "Cosmic Egg," according to which the universe started approximately 14 billion years ago as a tiny point. His prediction of the expanding universe was observationally confirmed soon afterwards in 1929 by Edwin Hubble. Lemaître's hypothesis of the origin of the universe, now called the "Big Bang" theory, has been verified by many observations and is the accepted view of the origin of the universe. See Grandpa's Glossary for Chapter 6 for more information on the Big Bang.

Andromeda Galaxy: See Grandpa's Glossary for Chapter 7

Asteroid that Killed the Dinosaurs: In 1980, scientists Luis Alvarez and his son Walter Alvarez proposed that the extinction of the land dinosaurs was caused by an asteroid that hit Planet Earth. Their proposal was based on a 65 million year old rock layer (the Gubbio layer) that has been found all over the world. The layer is the dividing line between older rocks below, in which dinosaur fossils are found, and newer rocks above, in which there are no dinosaur fossils. The clue to the asteroid impact as the source of the layer was its chemical composition, which was more like a meteor than normal earth rock. The conclusion was that this worldwide layer was caused by a major asteroid impact. A crater discovered in the 1970s on the Yucatán Peninsula of Mexico near the town of Chicxulub has since been identified as the likely impact site for the asteroid that killed the dinosaurs.

Chapter 13: Brainstorming

Cyanobacteria: Cyanobacteria are small, single-celled, bacteria organisms that live in water and manufacture their own food and grow by photosynthesis. They often grow in colonies large enough to see. Cyanobacteria are the oldest known fossils, 3.5 billion years old, but are still around today. They were essential in shaping the course of evolution on Earth, being responsible for the planet's oxygen gas concentration required by oxygen breathing life forms. Before the cyanobacteria generated oxygen in the oceans and atmosphere by photosynthesis, the planet was unsuitable for life as we know it today.

Photosynthesis: The most common photosynthesis is the process by which green plants. algae, and cyanobacteria use sunlight to synthesize foods (carbohydrates) from atmospheric carbon dioxide. Photosynthesis in plants generally involves the green pigment chlorophyll and releases oxygen gas as a byproduct. Photosynthesis changes sunlight into chemical energy in the form of carbohydrates.

Great Oxygen Event: Today's bird, insect, and land animal life on Earth is supported by an atmospheric oxygen concentration of 21 percent. But the early Earth had no atmospheric oxygen at all. Today's atmospheric oxygen concentration is the product of cyanobacteria. These single-celled organisms use carbon dioxide and water to produce carbohydrates and oxygen gas by photosynthesis using sunlight. Early cyanobacteria were largely in the oceans releasing oxygen that promoted the development of sea life. It was not until two billion years ago that the cyanobacteria started to release oxygen to the atmosphere. This time marks the start of the Great Oxygenation Event in which the oxygen concentration steadily grew to reach today's level. This event has supported the evolution of life as we know it today.

Chapter 14: Gathering Resources

Fusion Reactor: See Grandpa's Glossary Chapter 6 for information on the fusion reaction that takes place in stars and in the hydrogen bomb. When I took my first job in 1965, the company was working on a fusion process for a power plant. The problem is developing a way to contain the enormously high temperature for the reaction. Work on such a device is still in progress today with no practical solution. So, the Cosmic Egg fusion reactor is fictional.

Hydrogen Generator: The water molecule, which has one hydrogen atom and two oxygen atoms, can be split into hydrogen gas and oxygen gas using an electrical current. The process employs an electrolysis cell. The cell consists of two electrodes separated by an ion exchange membrane and often has a platinum catalyst. When a current is passed through the cell, the water in the cell is split into the two components which migrate to exit the cell at opposite electrodes.

Faster Than the Speed of Light: According to Einstein's Special Theory of Relativity, the speed of light in a vacuum is an absolute cosmic speed limit. Nothing can go faster. According to the theory, as an object approaches light speed, its observed mass gets larger and larger. So, more and more force is required to accelerate the object to approach light speed, In order to reach the speed of light, you'd need an infinite amount of force, and that's impossible! So objects cannot reach or exceed the speed of light.

Chapter 15: Building the Planet Colorado Space Station

Kepler Space Telescope: The Kepler space telescope, named for seventeenth century astronomer Johannes Kepler, was launched by NASA in 2009. Its mission was to discover Earth-size planets orbiting other stars in the Milky Way. Based on the data collected, NASA scientists estimated that there are 300 million stars with at least one habitable planet. The telescope was retired in 2018.

Hypothesis of the Cosmic Egg: See Grandpa's Glossary Chapter 6 for The Big Bang and Chapter 11 for Professor Georges Lemaître.

Chapter 18: The Five Most Unusual Things in the Universe

Black Holes: Black holes are super dense masses that, thanks to their enormous gravitational pulls, suck everything into them like enormous monster vacuums. Their gravity is so strong that even light can't escape. That's why they're black. Black holes were predicted by Einstein's General Theory of Relativity. There is a supermassive black hole at the center of our Milky Way galaxy. The biggest black hole is believed to have a mass of over 6 billion times the mass of our sun.

Dark Matter: Dark matter is one of the big puzzles in physics today. Dark matter is what we scientists call a fudge factor. We put it into our theories when the physics we know doesn't work. So, why do we need dark matter? Where does our physics not work? The answer is the structure of the universe. Normal physics says it shouldn't look like it does. Take a galaxy like our Milky Way. It is rotating like a pizza dough when the pizza guy throws it in the air. It gets bigger because of centrifugal force, which wants to push the dough away from the center. You feel that force when you stand at the edge of a merry-go-round. If you don't hold on, you fall off. Well, gravity is holding onto the stars at the edge of the Milky Way disk as it rotates. But gravity from the visible matter isn't enough to do the job. Our Milky Way would fly apart if the only gravity was from visible matter. Hence, the fudge factor. Let's assume there is enough extra matter to do the job of keeping the stars from flying off the galaxy. But we can't see it, hence the name dark matter. Calculations show that dark matter makes up more than 85 percent of the total matter in the universe.

Cyanobacteria: See Grandpa's Glossary Chapter 13

Photosynthesis: See Grandpa's Glossary Chapter 13

DNA (Deoxyribonucleic Acid): Let's say you wanted to build a robot. You look online and find a set of instructions. It would have to contain lots of things: a list of parts; specifications and drawings for each part (for size, shape, color, function, etc.); and instructions for how the parts are connected. If your friend is going to build one too, you need to copy the instructions. If you are building a complicated robot, the list could be very long, requiring a whole book full of instructions. The instructions for building you and all living things is contained in the DNA which is reproduced in every cell. The double-helix structure of DNA was identified by James Watson, Francis Crick, Maurice Wilkins, and Rosalind Franklin in separate papers in the journal *Nature* in 1953. Watson, Crick and Wilson (but not Franklin, who died in 1958) received the 1962 Nobel Prize in Physiology or Medicine. You can see a picture of the double helix in Epilogue 2. It is two long chains of molecules that are twisted around each other, like a long rope. The molecules are built of mainly 5 atoms: carbon, hydrogen, oxygen, nitrogen (CHON), as well as phosphorus. The building instructions are determined by the order or sequence in which the atoms of the elements are arranged, just as the twenty-six letters of the English alphabet can be rearranged to spell out thousands of different words. Each cell in your body contains a complete twisted pair of chains in the form of DNA. When you started life as a single cell, one of your DNA chains came from your mother and the other from your father. As your cells multiplied, the DNA was copied so that each cell had an identical copy of your first DNA molecule. The instructions on whether you are a girl or boy, the color of your eyes and hair, how tall you will be, and every other physical thing about you is coded in your DNA.

Evolution: Charles Darwin's theory of evolution was first presented in his book *On the Origin of Species* in 1859. Darwin described the process by which organisms change over time as a result of changes in inherited or behavioral traits. Changes that allow an organism to better adapt to its environment will help it acquire its needed resources to survive and have more offspring. This is the principal of *survival of the fittest*. What species is fittest may be dictated by changes in the environment, as is seen in numerous species extinction events where some species are better suited to the new environment. We now know that changes in an organism's DNA (mutations) can lead to alterations passed down to subsequent generations. This can sometimes lead to a new species that will be successful if it is fit for its environment.

Special Theory of Relativity: Albert Einstein's theory of special relativity was published in 1905. It explains how space and time are linked for objects that are moving at a constant speed in a straight line. One prediction of the theory is that as an object approaches the speed of light, its observed mass approaches an infinite value. This is the basis for Einstein's prediction that objects cannot go faster than the speed of light. Another famous prediction is the relationship $E=mc^2$ between mass (m) and energy (E), where c is the speed of light

General Theory of Relativity: General Relativity is the geometrical theory of gravitation published by Albert Einstein in 1915. When Einstein became aware that being weightless in the absence of gravity, or freely accelerating because of it, were equivalent and something extremely fundamental, he called it the "happiest thought of his life." This observation guided him in the development of the theory in which gravity is a geometric property of space. In Einstein's theory, mass tells space how to curve. and the curvature of space tells mass how to move. The General Theory of Relativity has important predictions. Georges Lemaître's solution of Einstein's equations for an expanding universe led to his Big Bang theory. The bending of light by gravity can lead to the phenomenon of gravitational lensing, in which multiple images of the same distant astronomical object are visible in the sky. The attraction of light by mass leads to the prediction of black holes, whose mass is so large that no light can escape. The theory predicts that cosmic events can produce gravitational wave distortions of space itself that travel at the speed of light. The first observation of gravitational waves was made by LIGO in 2015. The theory predicts the *Twin Paradox* described in Chapter 18. The predictions of general relativity have been confirmed in all observations and experiments to date.

NASA TESS YouTube video: https://youtu.be/85tdoDt1Qh0, TESS Catches its First Star-destroying Black Hole

How Big Are My Atoms video: See https://www.youtube.com/watch?v=jw1-wMR7JRM, on the STARDUST MYSTERY YouTube Channel

Light Years: The distances to other places in space are huge. For example, the distance from the Earth to the sun is 93 million miles; the distance to the closest star, Proxima Centauri, is 24 trillion miles; and the distance to the nearest galaxy, Andromeda, is 14 million trillion miles (14,000,000,000,000,000,000 miles). Astronomers decided that giving distances in such large numbers of miles or kilometers was not very easy for comparing different distances. So, they decided to invent a new unit of distance called the light-year. The light-year is the distance that light travels in one year. Since the speed of light is 186,282 miles per second, it travels 5.79 trillion miles per year. Proxima Centauri is 4.22 light-years away, and Andromeda is 2.5 million light-years away.

When looking at an object in a telescope, the light-year tells us something interesting besides distance. It is the time it took for the light we now are seeing to get here. So, we are really seeing how the object looked at some time in the past. When we see Andromeda in a telescope, we see how it looked 2.5 million years ago. When the Hubble telescope takes pictures of the furthest objects away from us, it is actually seeing what they looked like 13 billion years ago, not that long after the Big Bang. So, looking at objects that are further and further away lets us look at earlier and earlier times in the history of the universe.

Dark Matter and The Dinosaurs: In her book *Dark Matter and The Dinosaurs*, particle physicist Professor Lisa Randall of Harvard makes a case that dark matter had something to do with killing off the dinosaurs. Her proposal goes like this: When geologists and paleontologists look at the fossil records, there appears to be evidence that a major species extinction occurs every 30 to 33 million years. So, she asks, is there a physical reason to explain that? There is a physical event that has such a period. It is the oscillations of our solar system up and down through the plane of the Milky Way disk as it makes its way around the galaxy during its 225-million-year orbit. Each such orbit makes a galactic year. The idea is that the passage through the plane with its higher gravitational field might knock comets and asteroids out of their normal orbits around the sun, and some of these unhinged bodies might hit our planet. But calculations of this effect suggest gravity from normal matter is not sufficient to dislodge these objects from their orbit. Hence, she proposes that there is some extra gravity exerted by a disk of dark matter that lies within the disk of the visible Milky Way. The combined gravity from the normal matter disk and the dark matter disk might be enough to do the job.

Chapter 19: Finding the Sources of Stardust
Stardust Song Video: See https://www.youtube.com/watch?v=rmb3tQRfM9c, the STARDUST MYSTERY YouTube Channel

Fusion Reaction: See Grandpa's Glossary Chapter 6

Atom's Nucleus: At the center of every atom is the nucleus, which has almost all of the atom's mass. The nucleus is made up of positively charged protons and uncharged neutrons. The protons and neutrons are held together by the strong nuclear force. Electrons orbit the nucleus like the Earth orbits the sun, but not exactly, because the electron orbits are fuzzy clouds described by quantum mechanics. The size of the nucleus for hydrogen with one proton is about a trillion times smaller than a sand grain. The nucleus of uranium with 92 protons and between 141 and 146 neutrons is 10 times bigger than the nucleus of hydrogen. The size of the atom is more than 10,000 to 100,000 times bigger than the nucleus.

Chapter 20: The Universe Seven Billion Years Ago to Now
LIGO: See Grandpa's Glossary Chapter 2

Quasars: Quasars, or quasi-stellar objects, are extreme radio sources, emitting the energy of an entire galaxy or more. The power for Quasars appears to come from their super-massive black holes.

Continental Drift: Continental drift was a theory proposed in 1912 by Alfred Wegener, a geophysicist and meteorologist, that explained how continents shift positions on Earth's surface. The theory proposed that the present continents were once joined, forming a supercontinent called Pangaea. It explained why lookalike animal fossils, plant fossils, and similar rock formations are found on different continents. While details of how the continents moved were incorrect, the general ideas were important. Today, the theory of continental drift has been replaced by the science of plate tectonics that provides the explanation for how the continents move.

Pangaea: Pangaea was a supercontinent that existed over 300 million years ago. It was made up of all the continents that exist today. Pangaea began to break up about 175 million years ago as plate techtonics started separating the land mass into the separate continents of today.

Multi-Messenger Astronomy: See Grandpa's Glossary for Chapter 6

Chapter 21: The Universe Before Seven Billion Years Ago
Quarks: See Grandpa's Glossary Chapter 6

Chapter 22: The Big Bang and the First Atoms
Gluons: Gluons are particles that are part of the Standard Model of elementary particles. Like photons that travel back and forth between two charged particles to create the electromagnetic force, gluons do the analogous thing between quarks to create the strong force that "glues" the quarks together. Different quarks are glued in groups of three to form protons and neutrons.

Electromagnetic Force: The electromagnetic force is the force associated with electric and magnetic fields. It is the attractive and repulsive force associated with electrical charge that holds atoms and molecules together and participates in chemical reactions. It is the attractive and repulsive force associated with magnetism and all other electromagnetic phenomena. Like gravity, the electromagnetic force has an infinite range and obeys the inverse-square law. It is one of the four fundamental forces in nature, weaker than the strong nuclear force but stronger than the weak force and gravity.

Chapter 23: The Million Dollar Grand Prize
Theory of Evolution: See Grandpa's Glossary for Chapter 18

Epilogue 1: The Cosmic Kids Covid-19 Expedition 1: Infection
Cells: The cell is the basic building block for all living things. The cell was discovered by Robert Hooke in 1665 from studies of living material in which he observed very small repeating structures using a microscope. He called the structures cells because they resembled cells of a honeycomb. The first living things on Earth were single-celled organisms. Each cell was able to perform all the functions necessary for life. They could feed themselves and reproduce. Multicell creatures like humans have highly specialized cells that perform specific functions, such as nerve cells which are long and can transmit signals, muscle cells which contract to move arms and legs, and killer T-cells which can attack foreign objects to protect the body. Most cells are between 1 micron (1/1,000,000 of a meter) and 100 microns in size. The human body contains about 100 trillion cells whose size is like the thickness of a hair. An interesting website with interactive diagrams of cells is at http://www.cellsalive.com/cells/cell_model.htm.

Ribosomes: Ribosomes are complex structures found inside living cells. Their purpose is to produce functional substances or products (proteins) required by the organism according to the instructions contained in messenger RNA created by the organism. Viruses have the ability to hijack a cell's ribosomes to have it make copies of itself from its RNA. The ribosomes are also used by mRNA vaccines to have it make copies of the protein spikes seen on the outside of a coronavirus. The spikes stimulate the body's immune system to prepare it to fight off the virus should it appear.

Messenger RNA: Messenger RNA, or mRNA, is a single-stranded molecule of RNA that contains the genetic sequence of a gene, a part of the genetic code for a specific functional substance or product. For example, the protein spikes on the coronavirus are such functional products. The mRNA is read by a ribosome in the process of synthesizing the product. The pepsin molecule described in the Epilogue 2 chapter is another example of a functional product created by a cell's ribosomes using mRNA. The process of copying a gene from DNA into mRNA is called transcription.

Epilogue 2: The Cosmic Kids Covid-19 Expedition 2: Vaccine
Cell Nucleus: The cell nucleus is a highly specialized structure of every cell of living things. The cell serves as the information processing and administrative center of the life form. This structure has two major functions: it stores the cell's hereditary DNA material (the information on the organism's characteristics; the blueprint and instructions for its construction) in the genes, and it coordinates the cell's activities, which include growth, metabolism, protein synthesis, and reproduction (cell division).

IMAGES

Page 1: Image of the Coronavirus, Alissa Eckert, MSMI; Dan Higgins, MAMS; from the Centers for Disease Control and Prevention

Page 44: Background image of Colonel David Scott saluting the flag, NASA/JSC

Page 48 Image of Mercury, NASA Solar System Exploration, NASA/Johns Hopkins University Applied Physics Laboratory/Carnegie Institution of Washington

Page 49: Image of Venus, NASA Solar System Exploration, https://solarsystem.nasa.gov

Page 50: Image of Mars Rover, NASA Science

Page 51 top: Image of Jupiter NASA, ESA; A. Simon (Goddard Space Flight Center) and M. H. Wong (University of California, Berkeley)

Page 51 bottom: Image of Saturn, NASA, ESA; A. Simon (Goddard Space Flight Center), M. H. Wong (University of California, Berkeley), and the OPAL Team

Page 52 in Background: Image of Uranus, NASA Solar System Exploration, Hubble's Uranus, https://solarsystem.nasa.gov, NASA/Space Telescope Science Institute

Page 53: Image of Neptune, NASA/JPL

Page 54: Image of Pluto, NASA/Johns Hopkins University Applied Physics Laboratory/Southwest Research Institute

Page 103: Dwarf planet Haumea, NASA Solar System Exploration, NASA

Page 112: NASA TESS YouTube video, https://youtu.be/85tdoDt1Qh0

Page 119: Periodic Table / Jennifer Johnson January 9, 2017 https://blog.sdss.org/2017/01/09/origin-of-the-elements-in-the-solar-system/

Page 123: Image of Neutron Star, NASA, Dana Berry

LINKS TO OTHER PARTS OF
THE STARDUST MYSTERY PROJECT

THE STARDUST MYSTERY WEBSITE
https://TheStardustMystery.com

STARDUST MYSTERY YouTube channel:
https://www.youtube.com/channel/UCa5CQnZA6StFXXvEs418DKg
Science Videos
Game Trailers
How-To Videos

THE STARDUST MYSTERY VIDEO GAMES
https://store.steampowered.com/
MissionKT
Building The Universe

THE STARDUST MYSTERY ILLUSTRATED SCIENCE BOOK
Amazon:
https://www.amazon.com/dp/0578722194
Barns & Noble:
https://www.barnesandnoble.com/w/the-stardust-mystery-peter-solomon/1137747939?ean=9780578722191

NATIONAL SCIENCE FOUNDATION AWARD 1738291
https://www.nsf.gov/awardsearch/showAward?AWD_ID=1738291&HistoricalAwards=false

ABOUT THE AUTHOR

Peter Solomon, Ph.D., scientist and entrepreneur, is devoted to passing on his love for the many wonderful science stories to the younger generation. The birth of his twelfth grandchild was the inspiration for his first book and the STARDUST MYSTERY project which has created companion video games, science videos, and Expert Avatars that will answer questions about their lives and work. The theme of the Stardust Mystery story is: We are made of STARDUST that was once in the body of Albert Einstein and the last T-Rex. That is true. We each have more than 300 trillion carbon atoms that once belonged to and were exhaled by Einstein, and more than 5,000 trillion that were once in each T-Rex that roamed the Earth. And those atoms were created in the end-of-life explosions of stars. This new book set in the coronavirus pandemic continues that story. The same child characters make the best of their new life constraints and enter a new contest, The Race to the Big Bang. They, and hopefully the reader, will learn lots of new science. Peter lives in Connecticut with his wife Sally Moshein Solomon. Sally and Peter have had their vaccine shots and are now visiting with their grandchildren again.

CPSIA information can be obtained
at www.ICGtesting.com
Printed in the USA
JSHW031539240621
16214JS00003B/7